LOOK FOR THE RAINBOW

A Book of Religious Poems and Thoughts.

KINGSLEY C. NURSE

Look For The Rainbow
A Book of Religious Poems and Thoughts.
All rights reserved.

Copyright © 2020
Kingsley C. Nurse

Short Sweet and Subtle Books
P.O. Box 113042
Stamford, CT 06902

Printed in the United States of America

First Printing 2020
First Edition 2020

ISBN: 978-1-7351542-0-6
10 9 8 7 6 5 4 3 2 1

~ *Other Non-Religious Books by Kingsley C. Nurse* ~

The Many Minds of Me: A Book of Short Stories and Poems for the World, from My Mind

The Many Kinds of Glee: A Second Book of Short Stories and Poems for the World, from My Mind

The Black Awakening: A Novella.

The Speech of Animals: A Novella about Animals Talking.

The Self-Help Guru: A Witty Novella about Wits and Charm.

The Decision: A Short Novelette about the Choices we make.

The Infinity Span: A Short Novelette about a Boy's Strange Gift.

The Line Between Black and White: A Short Novelette about one big "What if?"

Thanks:

To God, for his unlimited mercy and love. To Jesus, for his eternal, unbounded compassion.

For:

My precious mother, who, once long ago, gave me a small copy of "The Prayer of Jabez". I want to honor her by publishing a like manner book, in hopes that someone, somewhere will read it, and perhaps, give a copy to their son, as my mother once did for me.

This Book is Dedicated:

To the love of people and faith. May you be brought closer to God in your life, by reading these words, and may you feel as I do, a hopeful love, from the Almighty Father, who is all-encompassing Love.

Table of Contents

Foreword

"At the end of the falling rain..."

When we're dealing with the hardships of life and experiencing loss and pain, it's always good to remember that God sees you. He knows your struggles and will always be there for you, even when times are tough.

Our part is to be *hopeful* and believe. We need to have faith. We should always hold the dream of tomorrow in our hearts, the hope of the future, and the hope of a better world.

That's why we look for the Rainbow.

This book is a compilation of my religious poems, a few religiously themed short stories, and my personal religious thoughts based on the teachings of the Christian faith and the wonderful things I have learned through studying the religious pioneers and inspired men and women of God in their books and writings of the past. This book is written with the purpose of love, and is meant to *sustain, uplift, motivate and encourage you.* As you turn through the pages, my hope is that you may find a poem or passage of text that speaks to you, so you may find peace, joy and comfort.

A religious poem is a lot like a song or a hymn. In truth, many precious hymns have arisen from the page of a *forlorn poet*, seeking only to pen the beauty of their faith to the world. This too is my *hope,* that one day these words may be read and even sung by you, not just through musical notes, but through a song in your heart...

God Bless.

-Kingsley

A Note On Publishing

Upon trying to seek out publishers to publish my work, I quickly became discouraged at finding that many, if not most Christian book publishers, no longer accept unsolicited manuscripts from unknown authors, that is, without representation by a literary agent or prior publisher credits from another press or imprint.

Further, to my greater dismay, when looking at literary agents to represent me, most make it clear that they do not look for poetry as one of the things they are willing to present to publishers. Finally, there are *publishers* who will look at an unknown writer of religious content, but demand quite fraudulently, a large sum of money from you, often greedily, to publish your hard work.

Ultimately, seeking to get your work out to the world is not as easy as one would think. This is true for secular work, and now apparently *even more so*, for religious content. This is where I found out that religious content publishing is just as competitive, if not more competitive, than secular work. This is *also* where I found out that religious poetry is seemingly not as desired by publishing presses as I thought they might be.

Personally, I feel this is a missed opportunity. There are many *excellent* works by excellent people, who only need a chance taken upon them. Now, there are certainly many, who will send in less than ideal work, along with some who will send in work akin to nonsense to see if it could be published, and as such, those things can spoil it for those who genuinely seek an outlet to publish.

Nonetheless, I understand the reasoning behind why publishing companies have to now limit the amount of submissions to their respective imprints. There is simply too many people to possibly get to. Too many manuscripts. Too many pages to sift through. I can see how that would quickly become overwhelming.

Now, while I am saddened that it is not as easy as I think it should be to get religious work published, I am happy to know that unknown authors like me still have an excellent chance, through self-publishing.

I am not resigned to resort to constant begging and placating to get my work out there. No. Not for this type of work. I am confident in my message, and my message is one of religious significance, no less than any other religiously published author. I will instead self-publish, and let my work speak for *itself*. I taught myself how to format, typeset and fully structure my own books, and I have already self-published several books. This I encourage all to do, if you are unknown, but still want your work to get out there.

Now my feelings towards this are the same for religious *and* for secular work. As mentioned above, I have already self-published secular work separately, and while I would love to have many people read my work, I don't force it. My work is out there in the world. When such a day comes, if at all, that someone discovers my writing, then so it is.

However, *this is religious work*. This is God's territory. If he wants someone to read your words that can bring someone closer to him, you can be certain they will. This is why I am confident that self-publishing my religious thoughts and poems will serve the same as being published by a large or well-known publishing house.

Now, I only offer my small book out to the world, in particular, for this book to be read with the only goal of encouraging and uplifting someone, *somewhere out there*, someone who desires to draw closer to God. I do not profess my words to be an authority on religion, and I am not a pastor or motivational speaker. I do however believe in the power of the Gospel, I believe in Jesus, and I believe that he will guide everything in the way he wants it to go.

Should my book end up in your hands, know that it is only a labor of love, as I present this book to you, through work all done by *myself*. I fully wrote, edited, typeset, and formatted this entire book to be published. I also designed and created the cover.

If I can do it, so can you.

Remember, God works in mysterious ways, and I trust him to allow my words to find their way to the eyes that he wants to see them.

Trust that God has a plan for your words too. Do not be discouraged. Write and take the effort to publish your work, whether by self or traditional means, for not one single word, written for God will be written in vain.

Not one *single* word.

I wish you many happy hours reading, and God's continued blessing.

Part I

A Few Uplifting Poems

"It is of the Lord's mercies that we are not consumed, because his compassions fail not. They are new every morning: great is thy faithfulness."

Lamentations 3:22-23 KJV

Mercy

As the olden workers bound in slavery once sang,

Their voices in harmony to the morning rang,

"O Lord have mercy on me!"

Seeking to put their trust and faith to rely on a token,

A promise they had faith would not be broken,

As they fell on their knees.

They knowing even then, betwixt persecution and pain,

Their prayers were never sent up in vain,

For The Lord in Mercy heard them.

Mercy! they cried. Languishing in ignorance but knowing
in part,

No one else could save their languishing heart,

Their bodies could be forfeit.

For their cry was not to be physically set free,
But of anguish of things we cannot see,
They desired fellowship with the Savior.

With nowhere to hide, and nowhere to run,
They fell on their face to the rising sun,
Asking for mercy for their souls.

How little we understand what mercy can mean,
How little our minds comprehend and glean,
The depth of love we forfeit.

Daily our cry should be as we seek to implore,
A small taste and portion of that everlasting store,
Of the Mercy that can save us.

An everlasting song of hope to rest upon,

May we all find grace and mercy struggling on,

As we fall on our knees.

The Father was Heartbroken

The Father was Heartbroken

When he lost his Son,

He who was with him before time begun.

As consecrated as himself, never to be undone.

The Father was heartbroken when he lost his son.

We lose our light

when our family is no longer here,

The object of our affections, our hearts are laid bare,

We take for granted the precious ones for who we care,

We lose our light when our family is no longer here.

The Father was heartbroken

When he lost his Son,

The Throne of the Almighty, of which he sat upon,

Delighting in him, whose face shined brighter than the
sun,

The Father was heartbroken when he lost his Son.

We cry in pain

when our loved ones are lost,

We were never designed to pay the price of sin or the
cost,

A gripping numbness akin to the deepest frost,

We cry in pain, when our loved ones are lost.

The Father was heartbroken

when he lost his Son,

We can never understand the pain he felt, even if infinity
was re-run.

Deep sadness he felt, for the He and The Father are
One.

The Father was heartbroken when he lost his Son.

We lose our strength

When our family members die,

Bitter pangs of anguish, we tearfully cry,

A tiny taste of the Almighty's infinite sigh,

We lose our strength when our family members die.

The Father was heartbroken

when he lost his Son,

Yet he did it for our sake, ensuring the battle was won,

A testament of love, when it is all said and done,

But The Father was still heartbroken when he lost his
Son.

Names Of Jesus

Savior.

Christ the Beloved.

The Son of God.

Hope of Earth.

Brother.

Immortal Counselor.

The Sap of Spring.

Prince of Peace.

Our Loving Leader.

The Compassionate One.

Rose of Sharon.

Joy of Heaven.

Immanuel, God with us.

Redeemer.

The Archangel.

The Sacrificial Lamb.

The Good Shepherd.

Friend.

You Already Lost

He paid the price, and covered the cost,

That's why you're done, you already lost.

Go on and keep spreading your hate to our kind,

But one day for you, hellfire you'll find.

You could have gone away, and left us alone,

You could have gone somewhere and eternally
atone,

We had nothing to do with you, you know this was
right,

But you plotted against us, in jealousy and spite.

So we fell for the lie, you got a small window in,

To make us go down with you in sickness and sin,

Now we suffer, without and deeply within,

For a short time, we were grouped with you as your kin.

But not anymore, One paid the whole price,

You played your hand, you rolled your dice,

You tried your best to win, but it simply didn't work,

You made a big stand, full horn and pitch-fork.

Just so everyone is clear, you don't look at all like this,

You more resemble a snake, speaking lies with a hiss.

To confuse us with tales, all absent of truth,

You liar, you grandstander, you utterly shameless sleuth.

Even your own hate you, they would destroy you and they should,

You had no right to trick them, they would take it back if they could.

But they made their choice too, so sadly they would,

Go down with you happily, a terrible choice, but understood.

Then a spectacular defeat, you lost on your own turf,

That's how sad and pitiful you are, go evaluate your self-worth

Chains are coming next, on you forever He will put,

That's why from the beginning, your head belonged under our foot.

When you realized you lost, you went away all mad,

Oh poor silly thing! Are you really sad?

There is no sympathy for you, do you know what you did?

A lost soul is infinity, gone forever, God Forbid.

But He paid the price, and he covered the cost

So try as you might, go on, have at it hoss,

Just a reminder for you, you and your foolish cause,

You are going to lose, but just so you know, you already lost.

Who Am I?

I am nobody. My life is not as special as it seems.

I am but a man, traversing this path as anyone else.

Suffering the pangs of temptation and pain as the rest of us.

I am sad, and broken, a vessel imperfect.

Seeking the one true way to lead me.

I look to the Lord to lead me.

My mind is a travernous wasteland of broken phrases,

And empty truths.

I wake up to vivid regrets of past hour claims.

Suffering the pangs of tempered questionings,

Just as anyone else.

Fighting like all who came before, and will come,

Thrust into a battle, not of my choosing,

Yet I must still live. As the Lord designed it.

I am a false advertisement,

seeking to portray who I am,

Falling much short of the grand example

I seek to set. It is still yet,

I know I am not alone in this,

For I put on a lucid, frivolous show, just like everyone else.

My life is time, passing as a speck of existence,

Waiting for my moment to come, then…to pass.

Then who am I?

A group of cells waiting to break down?

Or a fascinating specimen of prior accomplishments?

A broken vessel I am.

A silly, useless creature, briefly occupying space and breath.

Briefly occupying consciousness and depth.

Waiting for the Lord to save me.

Then who am I? I'm a child of God.

A person alive, someone who wants to thrive.

I am a human…a being.

Someone blind to the path,

But still seeing…how broken he is.

I am who I am. It's time for me to respect this,

And live, free of doubt and fear,

as God wants me to, and accept this.

The Conversation

One day, I had a conversation,
With the Almighty God alone,
He had granted me access to inquire of things,
Before his Holy Throne.

Before I spoke, He looked at my heart,
The answers were hard to hear,
He was sure to gently hold the bad,
And not make it more than I could bear.

I thought about what I wanted to ask,
I would not waste this opportunity,
Please God, can you show me the hidden truth,
Can you explain it all thoroughly?

"You cannot know the depth of truth
It is beyond your current means,
But I have given humanity plenty of proof,
Abundantly like sunshine it gleams."

To that I answered it doesn't provide,
An answer to who you are to Man;
It doesn't tell me what I want to know,
Nor does it help me understand.

Why must we suffer, why must it be,
Because we heeded the wrong voice?
Of the way we live, the way we die,
A final outcome of the choice?

"There is a purpose I made you yet,
You are not what I set you to be,
The pain, you will one day soon forget,
For you will be back with me"

I realized then, that God could provide,
The answer to all my questionings,
Instead, he chose to lovingly abide,
With my child-like mutterings.

Please tell me God, why do we feel,
Such sorrow and hurtful pain,
When I know you can easily turn off still,
Those sensors in our brain?

Or yet can I ask the reason why,

You do not give us wings,

We could simply go escape and fly,

From our pain and sufferings.

And importantly more, Why not give us back

The time we waste in life,

For you can break the immutable laws,

And bring me back my wife.

"What you want, for me is an easy task,

There are no "impossibles" with me,

But instead to you I simply ask,

Will that truly make you happy?"

"Your wife is gone, I know your pain,
I understand it intimately,
But your mind cannot begin to comprehend
That all emotions, come back to me."

But can't you change the dimensional laws,
A simple thought to dispatch,
The heavens and every single created being,
Erase all evil, then start from scratch?

Or I beg for the knowledge to obtain,
The vehicle to traverse time,
We could go back and fix it ourselves,
To make the world rewind.

We could then save the countless lost,

And warn of the bad to be,

To this, all humans would choose to do,

We would join in happily.

"You must never have, the chance to mold,

The flow of time so free,

You would simply destroy yourselves in a blink,

This is the truth, regretfully."

Then why must we suffer, when you are there,

You can save us from ourselves,

I would rather you take away my choice,

For evil, our nature compels.

"*You were made to be good, your heart was pure,*
You were only innocent in glee,
You chose to become, what you are now,
I let you choose, despite painfully."

"*You must know that I do not derive an ounce,*
Of pleasure to see you sad,
But I cannot remove your ability to make,
The decision to be bad."

"*It all comes down to the given choice,*
Of choosing to come to me,
I will not take away your right to choose
For then, you will never be free."

But God, it hurts so deeply to know,

We didn't have to suffer so much,

When will we get to leave this life,

And be closer to your touch?

I beg for comfort, please show me why,

We can't be saved right now,

I long to sit at your holy feet,

And in humble worship, bow.

I know you see our struggle to be,

I know you walk with us,

But can you come and end it all,

This whole experiment thus?

Our talk went long, time seemed to bend,

It seemed like a few minutes still,

For I was searching for the answers to justify,

His everlasting, immutable will.

Can I see, Dear God, an angel's light?

So I may keep the image in mind,

To that he answered with a soft "no",

For you would go irreversibly blind.

I asked what about the other worlds then,

Our science cannot tell us the truth,

I could show everyone the natural way,

With this irrefutable proof.

"I did not design for you to know,
What lies out in space so vast,
For you will try to meddle and tow,
Just as you want to change the past."

Then help me God, to understand,
Why evil gets its way,
This is the question everyone has,
In the world we live today.

Or tell me why we have to face,
The finality of the loss,
Of our loved ones dying in terrible pain
As your Son upon the cross?

"You must understand it is not the way,
Of my pronouncement and my decree.
In the garden with Eve and Adam I spoke,
As they stood there close to me."

"It was the choice you made to stray,
from the light of your innocent state,
The choice to disobey, then to sin,
This is what sealed your fate."

I know you won't remove the thoughts,
Of the evil, sinful man,
But surely you could work your part,
To change it, this you can.

But most of all, I regret the fact,

My precious mother is lost to me,

If you could give me just a little more time,

I would thank you so graciously.

Or send me in the distant past,

To see her once again,

Just to hug her and say goodbye,

For I missed the chance back then.

"I could easily give you what you ask,

But instead, I will say this,

You will once more see your mother bask,

In heavenly happy bliss."

But please, O God, I know you can,
Grant my longing request,
For this is the one thing I truly desire,
This gift would be the best.

He looked at me and quietly sighed,
I saw what no man has seen,
For God shed tears from his loving eyes,
Sorrowful tears, down his brow, between.

"My Child, you simply do not know,
The truth of your existence and race,
For whenever a human suffers in pain,
I take half and instantly erase."

"I bring it back to me and keep,
The painful sorrow that you feel,
For humans cannot bear the deathly pangs,
Of the true pain of sin for real."

"But I will tell you one last thing,
Before you leave this place,
I went back in time and blew a peaceful breeze,
On your mother's dying face."

I knew the time was almost come,
To end the precious talk,
He said I could return once more
For now, with me, he'll walk.

We walked and spoke of many other things,
We talked until the dawn,
I will end this poem to you, for now,
For it is simply already too long.

Perhaps another time, I'll share with you,
The conversation God had with me,
If you come once more and give me your ear,
I will share it then, *happily*.

Peace

So much to worry about, so much to process,

My mind is in constant flux,

Working, remembering, solving,

Putting pieces together, making sense of it all.

Frustrated, I walk to the front and open my door

There I am greeted by a view unlike no other,

A calm, gentle wind, rustling past green lively leaves,

Swaying back and forth in connection to us.

For in the stillness of the wind, in the beauty of that calmness,

My mind can slow down.

I look further still, and see a wall of beauty,

Incomparable to anything else,

A panoramic view of gentleness and hope,

Invading my senses and pushing away the cares of the present,

Leaving me with a sense of the inert concept,

That everything we do is guided by an eternal providence.

The sky remains unbelievably blue,

And the animals go about their day.

I stand there, fixated in the moment of consciousness,

Kept in balance with the one singular thought,

That in the stillness of the wind, in the beauty of that calmness,

My mind can be at ease.

And for that one fleeting moment in time,

I can experience a little bit of what we know as *peace*.

The Infinity Hallway

I close my eyes and am transported to a place,

Full of memories and grace,

A place I call the infinity hallway.

There I find long stretching lengths,

Full of white, open doors.

There, my memories are kept.

All doors open to me, to enter at will.

I walk along the infinity hallway,

Walking in and out of doors,

seeing past images and thoughts of my life.

I am grateful and sad,

For these doors grant me unlimited access to experience my memories

Over and over again.

The good and the bad alike.

As I walk the infinity hallway, I enter a length where the doors are open,

And I see all the memories of the one who bore me, my mother.

These doors are open and clear,

I enter joyously each one,

Seeing her smile and remembering her voice.

I walk along, gliding back and forth,

In and out of each door,

Happy to see what is not easily seen,

Remembering these things as they once had been

Only residing now in your mind,

Locked away from normal access, but kept secure forever.

I walk the infinity hallway, spending as much time as I need in each entrance,

Just as happy as entering the last one,

Until I reach a stretch of the hallway,

Where things are not as happy as before,

Where illness and pain awaits behind that open door,

I skip several of them, no longer happy to relive the agonizing permanence they maintain.

I walk still yet, until I reach a stretch of closed white doors,

I realize that here is where my memories of her stop,

For I had been skipping past several doors.

As I turn back, searching for the last open door,

Seeking to find the point of my last memory of her,

I desperately search and find it.

There the door lay open and clear,

A sad melancholy cloud in the air,

An arrangement of chairs, as I sit amongst my father, brothers and sisters at a funeral.

This is the last open door in that section.

I do not bother to enter, for those memories do not need to be re-lived.

Neither the prior several doors.

For in them contain the news I didn't want to hear,

And the preceding days directly after it.

I walk ahead, seeking to get past the section altogether,

Walking ahead to leave that sad, dreadful length,

And arrive back at the area of closed doors.

I then understand. These doors are closed,

for I have no more remaining living memories of her to see.

I run forward, viewing other sections as I glaze by, catching up to the present,

Until I stand, paradoxically so,

Looking at myself, as in two mirrors turned towards each other,

Viewing myself, looking at myself, in the infinity hallway.

I turn around to try to scan the full length of the path I traveled,

Knowing full well I can't.

Surprisingly so, as I turn around again, I see millions, no billions, even trillions and more,

Of open doors ahead,

My eyes able to see and visualize the length,

And some I see are open and bright,

Yet I cannot discern what is inside until I walk there,

So I begin to walk there, heading in the direction of infinite open doors.

No longer fighting to see only what I remember,

A fire is lit in me, like a glowing ember.

For now I want to see what the future holds.

My eyes seemingly getting stronger as I walk,

Heading towards the future of the infinity hallway.

I stop in surprise, for I begin to see, far, far up ahead,

A glimmer of an image too happy to put into words.

I run towards that section, but I seemingly am unable to get beyond tomorrow's doors.

I want to get there desperately.

For I see an open door, distant from me, way up ahead in the path,

With me and my siblings and my father,

All standing around my mother once more,

In a happy embrace.

What Did He See?

What did he see? A being of infinite power and knowledge,

Deciding willfully to cast off that cloak of shining immortality and strength,

Second only to his Father.

What did he see, as he watched a trillion, trillion beings of light he created,

gather in opposition against him?

Looking at each of their jealous, misled and troubled faces,

Knowing their fate?

What did he see, as he watched innocent children doom themselves to death,

When they didn't have to.

Knowing he had already decided to do what he would do, if they made the decision to die?

Now, choosing to walk on the dirty dust of the ground,

Especially since this entire universe is beneath him.

Knowing full well, that everything is nothing to him but a speck, and not even that.

Taking on an infant's form at first,

Looking at humans as they thus held him.

Relying on them for his sustenance and care, when he didn't have to.

Taking on a form weaker than anything now in creation,

Occupying a weakened body, miraculously sustained.

Humbly allowing himself to feel the pain and irritations of creatures who deserve it.

Electing to stay and live amongst us, a God in human form,

Now born as a baby looking at its mother.

Looking up at her, laying there in the full capacity of God-hood,

    contained within a human mind.

    Infinitely held in place by his divine power,

    Lest that human part should crumble.

    What did he see, as he walked around as a child,

    Looking at the adult humans he thus created?

    Watching them look at him as he read their thoughts,

    and could hear the whole world at the same time.

    Knowing the events of their lives as it will happen In the future,

    Since he already determined it.

    Seeing them walk towards a tomorrow directed by this simple child's will?

    What did he see? As a man, seeing beings of light flying all around everyone,

    smiling at him and bowing, longing to intervene when he suffered pain, but instructed by him earlier not to interfere,

As he carried out his mission.

Hearing them scream out in anger and frustration.

Or to see the entire universe as he looked up at the sky,

and at the same time converse with other worlds?

Or was it designed that he would be absent from them for a time?

Allowing them to watch on, as he carried out his mission.

What did he see, as he watched an angel he created,

Disrespectfully tempt him and try to get him to fail,

Knowing full well that he won't fail.

Watching that angel look at him in jealousy and spite,

For no reason whatsoever.

What does he see now? As we pray to him and ask for the strength,

To endure what he endured?

Knowing the future of himself embracing his blessed, loved ones in heaven's bliss?

To him, that future is now, for he isn't bound by time.

To see his children bowing at his feet,

thanking him for his infinite sacrifice.

He explaining that he already saw it all, even back before they were created.

Can we even begin to imagine what he saw?

Dear merciful Lord, we hope one day you will tell us,

As we look at you and ask you,

What did you see?

The Missed Opportunity

I gave up the right to teach an innocent mind,
The love of God for them,
What awaits my soul, is guilt I find,
For I chose to neglect a precious gem.

My soul is tortured, for I lacked the strength,
To do what I once was driven,
My mind constantly battered at length,
As I struggle to keep the gift I was given.

A moment to decide, a soul to save,
A missed opportunity so great,
A light to shine in a dimly lit cave,
A chance to unseal a soul's fate.

That soul wandering on, in the bitter cold,
Of living, deprived of light,
Living outside the Good Shepherd's fold,
Stumbling on blind, without sight.

I've neglected my chance, I see the loss,
I long for another chance to atone,
For my neglect comes at a very high cost,
The bitter seeds that I have sown.

Another chance, I pray, deep in my heart,
The opportunity to do the right thing,
Dear Lord, have mercy, as I do my part
A chance to God, a soul to bring.

Qualities Of God

Slow to Anger, Swift to bless,

With Abundant Mercy,

And Faithfulness.

Never-ending Goodness,

Unconditional love as proof,

Also Abundant in Truth.

Compassion of heart,

Understanding of Pain,

The True Breaker of the Chain.

A Lover of Life,

A Listening Friend,

The only One whom your heart can mend.

Infinitely strong,

and Infinitely Wise,

Someone who never, ever lies.

Keeper of your trust,

Abounding in Good,

The One Who always understood.

A caring Father,

Loving from the start,

The owner of the Biggest Heart.

The Light of Life,

With the Cover of a Dove,

The Habitation of Unceasing Love.

Look For The Rainbow

At the edge of the clouds, at the end of the falling rain,

Look for the Rainbow.

There we will lose our anxiety and our fear.

Because it will always be there.

You'll never search for it in vain,

Since it only appears after the sunny rain.

So look for the Rainbow.

It's not hard to find. It's always in the same spot.

Just scan the skies a little, you don't have to look around a lot,

Just look for the Rainbow.

Across from the sun, and shining on a cloud,

After the thunderclaps, and strikes of lightning loud,

Look for the Rainbow.

Look carefully and quickly, for soon it will go.

Representative of the promise given long ago;

So look for the Rainbow.

The colors of every spectrum of light, prism-ly shining ever so bright,

A bow of hope and treasure,

At the change of the rainy weather,

A promise that will be kept forever,

That's why we look for the Rainbow.

And Thus We Are With Thee

The only reason we are free
Is because God's gift came to be
A token of his love for man,
He covered and paid our fee.

A Song of a heart that is free
Dear Jesus, we need to see
That we cannot without you be,
And thus we are with thee.

Tossed about in the roaring sea,
I need you to be with me.
I hunger for life, open and un-spanned,
I hunger for the fruit of the tree.

A Song of a heart that is free

Dear Jesus, we need to see

That we cannot without you be,

And thus we are with thee.

I pray for everyone to see,

Each one to some degree,

That we are cared for by his love,

By the providence of eternity.

A Song of a heart that is free

Dear Jesus, we need to see

That we cannot without you be,

So thus we are with thee.

The despair of sin I would flee,

This I pray for passionately.

That he will cover me like a dove,

For this is my longing plea.

A Song of a heart that is free

Dear Jesus, we need to see

That we cannot without you be,

So thus we are with thee.

And thus we are with thee.

Beautiful (A Poem For My Mother)

A lovely flower put upon this earth,

Not of rich, or royal or noble birth,

Sent to live a hard and simple Christian life,

As someone's mother, and someone's wife.

When in throngs of joy she would proclaim,

She loved Jesus's wonderful and holy name.

And she would proclaim, yet in earnest and dutiful,

The things she saw were *abundantly beautiful*.

She only wanted to live, and appreciate the beauty,

Of this wonderful earth, a concept of the duty,

given to all, to see what exists in nature,

A remnant of the past's lovely golden caricature.

She persevered and attained the hallmark of college,

A symbol of the beauty she found in knowledge,

When in joy she would proclaim in earnest and dutiful,

The knowledge she obtained to be quite *endearingly beautiful.*

For a time she lived happily, as most people will,

But then struggling on, despite sickness and still,

To take care of her children until they were grown,

And give them a precious seed, to plant happiness of their own.

She loved all things holy, and all things bright,

Of words written in poems, she also loved to write.

When in joy she would proclaim, in earnest and dutiful,

The thing she just read to be *graciously beautiful.*

She gave her all, to her life and duty,

To show her faith, and appreciate the beauty,

of who she was, loving, gentle, and kind

A vision of the strong person I saw in my mind.

Trusting in God to one day raise her in glory,

This poem, a small tribute to her life story,

For in times past, she would proclaim in earnest and
dutiful,

The hope of the Lord's return as *immensely beautiful.*

The time did come, and she was taken,

As the Lord felt she did enough, but she was never
forsaken,

Passing quietly in her sleep, as she painlessly went,

An angel hovering by her side, touching her calmy as
he bent.

Leaning in life, on the everlasting token,

She possessed a faith that could never be broken,

When in joy she would proclaim, in earnest and dutiful,

The life that she lived was *remarkably beautiful.*

In quiet peace, and happiness in faith she rested,

Knowing that all her strength was wisely invested,

In possessing the sight, to see beauty so wide,

Knowing that the Lord never left her side.

She is gone for now, but I see her in the past,

I go back and remember the time we spent last,

When at times I would proclaim in earnest and viewtiful,

Her smile was always bright and *stunningly beautiful.*

She never lost her faith while she was alive,

to recognize the struggle, yet continue to strive,

To see beyond what in life is surely undisputable,

The sustaining fact that God's Love for her is
immutable.

So I remember her now, when in thoughts I am bound,

I would recall her lovely voice and precious sound,

As she always to my delight, proclaimed in earnest and
dutiful,

The things she found to be *wonderfully beautiful.*

You Can Save Us

You can save us with your love,

If not, we perish thereof,

Please Lord, impart from above.

Send your spirit like a dove.

You can save us with your grace,

We can survive only by your face,

We seek your heart to interlace,

And provide us strength for this race.

You can save us with your blessing,

A token of your warmth on us caressing,

Only to you, our love confessing,

For you are the only one for us, intercessing.

You can save us with your heart,

We wait for your mercy to impart,

To live for you in faith, to start,

To spread your love and do our part.

You can save us with your power,

Do not leave us, lest evil devour,

As we move on, our enemies cower,

We rely on your strength every hour.

You can save us with redemption,

Paying our price, in pre-emption,

All who believe are granted exemption,

Given in perfect condescension.

The Compassion That Never Ends

Jesus thou art all compassion,

If not for thee, we perish,

Thou, who had the only power to come to our aid,

Planning to do it even before we needed it.

Your mercy never, ever ends.

We will forever praise your love for us,

Something we did not deserve,

But granted us out of your blessed, forgiving heart.

Jesus thou art all compassion.

When upon the moment you knew we fell from grace,

A sad expression fell upon your lovely face.

Knowing we would perish.

But you deemed it not so.

You mercifully deemed it not so.

You would not stand by while we were destroyed.

Even though the infinite law demanded it,

Because your mercy never ends.

You took our wretched race and sacrificed it all for us.

Something we can never fully appreciate,

For all of eternity and beyond.

We can only dedicate ourselves to you,

And give you a free soul,

Which can never be enough to repay.

Only by a gift from you, we received,

The grace we can only barely comprehend.

The grace that will allow us to see your blessed face,

When time comes to an end.

Our tears we shed in gratitude to you,

For you have held and sustained us,

By your compassion that never ends.

Part II

A Few Religious Thoughts

"For I know the plans I have for you," declares the Lord, "plans to prosper you and not to harm you, plans to give you hope and a future."

Jeremiah 29:11 NIV

Hopeful Thoughts

I am deeply religious, and I have a deep belief in God. I believe that Jesus died for man's sins, and that one day, he will come back again for us and save us from life on this planet.

I truly believe in this.

Now, we should always have hopeful thoughts, despite how bad things may get in this life.

So how do you have hopeful thoughts? And how do you keep the faith even though the world seems to want to lead you otherwise?

Well, for one, even if you aren't religious, just know that there is certainly more good than evil in this world, despite our constant exposure to evil and the things we see.

Now, as I mentioned above, we have been hearing for forever that Jesus will come back soon. This is one of the core principles of my faith, and our hope and faith itself, rests upon this *single* promise.

But when? After all, I want to see my loved ones again. I want to go to heaven.

Well, we have the bible and prophecy from books like Matthew, Timothy and Revelation. They all showcase and expound upon what the world will look like in the *last days*.

The last days, before Jesus comes again.

Now I won't lie to you. *Things will get pretty bad*. But for now, life will continue on. *Until then*, we have the rainbow.

We have to keep hopeful thoughts in our hearts until such time comes when the future becomes the present. And if our current generation does not see the fulfillment of the promise, then we pass down our faith to the new generation, always knowing in faith that one day, Jesus will appear.

So do not despair, my friend. Know that the sky will **always** be blue. Know that there will *never be a time when all people* will accept evil and wrongful acts.

It will come a time in the distant future that those people may be in a minority, but the world will never,

ever be rid of good, God-fearing people, *never*. There will always be someone standing up for good and what is right. Come what may.

The coming future is bright, not bleak.

Now, as a man, I wholeheartedly believe in Science, as all men should. Science should not conflict with religion, but *compliment* it.

However, I know that mankind will *never* go extinct, no matter what existential derivatives we expound upon. The sun will *never* supernova and destroy the planet, not even billions of years later.

A meteor will never crash into us and wipe us all out. We may live through terrible times, and worse may be yet to come, but ultimately the human race will one day be happy.

One day.

Now isn't that a *hopeful* thought?

Courage and Fear

So yes, we are human. We get scared. This cannot be helped.

But you do not have to let the fear you feel consume or control you.

We first experienced fear at the loss of our innocence, when God, in all his glory and majesty, would come every afternoon and visit Adam and Eve in the garden of Eden and ask them what they learned for the day.

Now, God's presence is not a joke. When the Deity of the Universe goes somewhere, there is immense thundering, fire, lightning, earthquakes and terrible, immense natural ceremony going on.

It just happens. This is a by-product of his presence. This is not some show. God cannot be introduced by any other being in the Universe with enough respect to properly compliment him.

Seriously. You know, since he is God.

Nothing comes before him. *Nothing.*

So whenever God goes somewhere, he literally has to announce himself. No other being, besides, Jesus himself can announce or introduce the Father.

God is great and terrible. We cannot fathom the immense, infinite majesty and *unlimited* power he has.

Not even in eternity, for God is beyond *infinity itself.*

Think about that.

Every day, when God came to visit, with all the proceedings of majesty and infinite power, Adam and Eve gladly received him, as they were innocent, and had nothing to fear. They had not sinned, so they had the privilege of looking upon Jesus himself in all his divine majesty and glory, uninhibited.

Now you may wonder why I interchange God and Jesus as God? Because Jesus is God. God is also God. God the Father and Jesus the Son are One.

This is not debatable or discussable.

When Jesus showed up in front of Adam and Eve, they happily told him all they learned from the day.

But the one day they sinned, they could not stand to welcome the presence of the divine.

Why? Well one, they were afraid. They literally noticed the immense procession that followed him as he approached. It was not something a now fallen being can withstand.

And two, they also were guilty. They knew they had disobeyed and couldn't face the Creator.

So they cowered in fear.

God knew they had already done it before he came to them of course, but he still wanted them to see the awful consequences of their disobedience. Now, we will know **true** fear. Innocence lost.

However, it does not mean he wanted us to be consumed by fear *forever.*

It hurt God's heart to see happy, created beings, now terrified at his presence as he walked towards them. How do you feel, when your child or pet is scared when they see you approaching when they did something wrong?

Yes, you know they should be afraid, for they did something wrong, but does it not hurt your heart to see your little one or loved pet afraid to see you coming?

Do you take pleasure in seeing them cry in guilt and fear, knowing you will be mad at them? Can you even imagine the level of pain, that God, who is infinite love, has experienced since our creation? We cry at heartache and pain of unrequited or lost love. But we know nothing of *true infinite broken hearts.*

Hearts who loved their creation beyond comprehension to give up God-hood for.

Reader, I tell you now, there are things we simply have no idea of, and will never know, until we get to heaven.

God has, through communication with man, mentioned that we should be strong and not afraid anymore. We should not be fearful, but courageous. Why? Well, being afraid constantly puts us in that cowered position of not being under the protection of God anymore.

The thing is, we *are* under his protection. Jesus died for our sins, so now, we can talk to God. We do not have to be afraid.

Not anymore.

He will hear us when we attempt to talk to him.

This is important, because God wants us to know we do not have to cower as Adam and Eve once did when we seek to come to him. We can approach freely, because of Jesus. We cannot look at his face just yet, but we can look *towards* his face.

Back in the garden, Adam and Eve could not even do that, *out of fear.*

Do you understand? Do you begin to fathom even slightly, how terrible of a mistake we made?

One day, we will be able to confidently and joyfully welcome the presence of the Almighty, with all the thundering and fire and earthquakes and terrible procession that accompanies him. For now, we must behave courageously and approach, in courage and faith, but still accepting our place for now, as not having full direct conversation with God, but through faith and belief in Jesus, who died for our sins, we have a chance to be brought back in direct *communication* with him.

Love, Hate and Jealousy

God is Right. His reasons for doing things are perfectly and always *completely* justified.

The devil is wrong. And yes, he knows it.

God loves us *infinitely*. Jesus loves us *infinitely*. The devil, hates us *intensely*.

And why? Did we do anything in particular to him? Nope. Nothing. We did absolutely nothing to him. He literally stared at us from afar and got jealous of us.

All because we were happy. Oh, and innocent.

He wanted to corrupt an innocent being that God had *just* created.

All to spite God.

Did you know that after he was kicked out of heaven, he thought about all that he lost, and he requested an audience with Jesus to ask to come back. Jesus, being the beloved wonderful merciful one that he is, granted him a last request to talk about it.

Seriously. It happened. This is not made up.

At the meeting, the devil begged Jesus and said he was "sorry" and he wouldn't do it again.

He was lying.

If Jesus allowed him back, he would have done the same thing again. He would have worked up the nerve the once again cause more angels to fall. Why? Because he secretly hated Jesus in his heart, and was jealous of him. God knew this.

But how could you hate infinite love? How could you scorn unbounded compassion?

Even unexplainable yet, how could you hate the creator that made you fourth in line in power?

Seriously. Fourth in line in power. God the Father, Jesus the Son, God, The Holy Spirit, then him.

Yes, he was next in power. He literally was next in power in all of the Universe.

Crazy right?

After Jesus told him he could not come back, because he could not take the chance of him corrupting the two-thirds of the Angels that were left, he threw the equivalent of a temper tantrum and literally "overturned the proverbial table" and started cursing God again and calling Jesus and God a tyrant.

Jesus left the meeting with him there, still cursing.

So now, you ask, why do I tell you this? Because we should know what happened before we were created, and why he tempted us to disobey God. He wanted to corrupt an innocent thing. He couldn't force Adam to eat the fruit, but he made every effort to convince us to do it.

He was told that he has a fixed time to exist, and that one day he will be destroyed. So now the devil wants to do one thing, and one thing only: *drag as much of us down with him as possible.*

He, along with the angels who are lost with him only want to see other human souls alongside them when the time comes for them to be destroyed. *We are just a number to them.* Seriously. They only want to see as much human souls lost with them to take an evil twisted satisfaction right before they are destroyed. This is how much he hates us. How much he hates God.

For Jesus will indeed be hurt infinitely by the loss of your soul.

You can avoid that. Do not be a number they can draw satisfaction from when they are about to get their end.

Trust God. *Believe in God.* Trust in Jesus. He already told us what to do.

Do not allow your soul to be lost.

Sacrifice, Selfishness and Selflessness

Jesus made the ultimate sacrifice for us. This does not register to our simple, feeble minds, but he seriously did.

Imagine, the Sovereign God of the Universe coming down to an insignificant planet to save the people there? Seriously, we are nothing but a speck of dust, and not even that. If you doubt me, go look at those *"Size of the Universe"* videos all over YouTube. You'll see.

I'm gonna say something infinitely scary.

Jesus could have *failed*. Not because he wasn't capable or could not do it.

Rather, he could have given up. Yes. He could have given up when he felt all the sin of the world on his head, and the literal weight of all the guilt of the human race from the moment we sinned, even to the future.

We could not bear that. Trust me. No one person alive then or now could have. Only God could have.

Seriously, It was a lot.

And even though it was God bearing it, you do know, that he asked to have it taken away.

I will say it again, the load was NOT light. God himself asked to have it removed.

Yes, the infinite compassion, the unbounded love, the immeasurable mercy of mercies himself, asked for it to be taken away, and only accepted it, as it was the will of the Father.

We simply cannot grasp the seriousness of this, or how close we came to full destruction.

If God had looked at Jesus and said, "You know what? Nope. You are not suffering a single *femtosecond* more." We would be done. Destroyed. No hope. It would have been all over.

And we would have deserved it.

The devil would have won, and it would have been proven that God could not sacrifice for the objects of his affection.

Do you understand this? *Do you?*

Do you understand that it was only infinite love that saved us in that exact very moment? We literally came that close to *full and utter destruction*. This is not a joke.

We should be on our knees nonstop just thanking Jesus for literally not giving up. Had he looked up to his father and said, "I don't want to anymore." He would have been taken back to heaven instantly. Yes, instantly.

You think God could not destroy ALL of creation and start again? Think about that. If he wanted, he could simply blink the entire universe out of existence and save his son. Angels and all. This is not a joke.

God is *not* selfish. No matter who or what anyone says.

The infinite God watched as his son was *tortured* and *beaten* and *slapped* and *spit on*, and *kicked*, and *punched* and *whipped* and *stabbed*, so we wouldn't be destroyed.

If your precious son or daughter or brother or sister, or close relative or friend you loved so much, was going through something like that, and they looked at you and *cried* and asked for it to stop, and you had the power to stop it *instantly*, could you keep watching?

You already know the answer. Think about this and thank God right now. Seriously. *Right now.*

For he is the most unselfish being in the entire universe.

Nothing matches the infinite Father. Not in *Love*. Not in *Mercy*. Not in *Longsuffering*. Not in *Selflessness*.

Pride and Slavery (And why God hates both)

There is a reason God hates pride the most.

It is the single defining trait that caused the destruction of souls, a loss of infinite variety.

Yes. One single soul lost is infinite variety lost.

God is *immeasurable.* He planned and created each soul alive or that ever was alive. He deemed that not one single soul should be lost, even though we sinned.

That's why Jesus was sent to die for our sins. He died for the past and the future.

It is the choice of man, the God-given choice to give their soul to the devil.

And so the soul that sinned will finally die.

God wanted to save us all. But we had to want to be saved. We had to want to accept his rescuing.

Unfortunately, there will be souls lost. God could prevent this, but it would take away the one line God deemed he would never cross.

Choice.

Seriously. He would never make automatons or robots who did whatever he told them to, with no choice. He rather put the choice of it all to the being he created, to choose to worship and love him of his *own* volition.

This is true and *complete freedom.*

Even if it costs a soul, it is an unbreakable contract God imposes on all living creatures. If he broke it, the devil wins the eternal argument. The argument that God seeks to control creatures by his will. This is false, and is only what the devil wants, but he falsely accuses God of this.

The devil will *never* win that argument.

God never created slaves. He has never wanted creatures to be forced to serve him. It is a shame we humans once desired slaves, when the Father of the Universe did not.

And the funny thing? Pride is what caused it all. There was a time in heaven, when it came the moment of truth. The devil, still lucifer, was in heaven and did not go too far. He was in the wrong of course, but he could have turned back and forgotten about his feelings of dissent. He could have simply accepted the order of things, as it was right, and go back to being a happy angel.

But no.

He was *too prideful.*

Too prideful to go back and simply apologize for being wrong. Too prideful to stand in front of all the angels and tell them he was in the wrong and that for the first time, they must disregard his words. The rest of the angels loved him and it would not have changed *anything* if at all, but he refused. He refused to admit wrong.

Thus we are as we are now. A terrible consequence of the choice of pride.

Yes, a choice the devil made.

Is it any wonder that God also imposed the only restriction to be absolved and forgiven of sins, is to *ask* for that forgiveness and *admit* to your sin?

This is not a joke, nor is this a coincidence.

God designed it to be that way. He wants us to show that we are sorry for what we did. The sin we committed. Then ask for forgiveness.

This way, if we can simply do this, even once, we are *infinitely* stronger than the devil.

For he could not do it.

We are imbued with God's spirit and his love. We are still and always will be, free souls. Even though we sinned and fell short of his grace, we can still come to him and ask for forgiveness, and admit to our sin.

If we choose to.

We are better than the devil. You are a child of God, a sibling of Jesus. A relative to omnipotence *itself.*

You can do it. Go to God right now and ask for forgiveness. Literally just stop and pray in your mind and tell Jesus that you are sorry. Tell him you admit to wrong-doing. It doesn't have to be specific right now.

Just admit to it. Then ask for forgiveness, through Jesus.

For only through Jesus can our sins be forgiven. There is no other way. No matter what anyone says to the contrary. No matter what.

Some people may not like to hear this, but as sure as you are reading this, It has to be Jesus. Only Jesus. I'm *dead* serious.

If you do this, and I know you can, you will have overcome the most devastating sin, the sin the devil could not overcome.

You would have overcome *pride.*

Happiness, Unhappiness and God's Plan

So things haven't been going well for you and you are unhappy.

Life has been tough. Still yet, for others, it appears that their entire existence has been one of torture, pain and unhappiness.

Young, innocent children starve. People are murdered and brutally killed. The majority of life amounts to a collective sum of an unfair life for many.

Surely you have a reason to be unhappy.

Sadly, you do not.

Yes, you heard me right. And yes, I know, this is harsh. Especially for someone who has undergone immense hardships in life. Someone who has battled the tide of unending suffering and pain this world has to give.

But still, you must not deem to be unhappy. There are many reasons for this.

However, the main reason is that you are alive. And yes, even sometimes in pain and discomfort.

God knows, by the way. It will all make sense one day.

Not now, but one day.

Yes, *one day.*

For now, we must remember that we are alive. We are alive to still appreciate life and praise God. God in his infinite wisdom determines all.

He does not deem man to suffer, but nothing can take place without God determining it should happen.

So then, the question comes up of cruelty by a God who sees and allows his children to suffer.

God does not make his children suffer. *We must remember this.* It is our choice that caused this. This is very important to remember this. *God did not pre-ordain suffering.* It was us who caused it.

Now, you are alive, yet in pain. You are conscious, but you suffer.

Still, you must thank God. For he determined to have you exist. Yes, in the grand scheme of eternity, you, your sole, *single self,* existed in the construct of the benevolent universe God created.

As such, only a created being can boast this.

Now again, I understand that this is not much comfort to the starving child, or the stricken person with Cancer, or the victim of a crime or vile act upon them by another person, but it is important for us to remember that through it all, if we remember that God has a plan for everyone, and a purpose for all, we can derive a comfort in the Almighty, that one day you will be rewarded for your hardships. Not in the sense that you *must* suffer to receive reward, but *because you suffered* yet trusted in his infinite, omniscient wisdom, you are rewarded.

It is simply not for us to know the full pieces of the puzzle right now. God does not want that. He wants us to have faith and trust in him.

Why? Well, it was our sin, not of seeking to become like God or require forced obedience through haughtiness and pride like the devil, but of *distrust* to God.

Yes, our sin was simply distrust. Distrust by disobedience.

Had we listened; we would not have been in this state now. It is our disobedience that is the result of the collective sum of the pain experienced by the human race.

I'm serious. It was simply distrust.

So blame Adam? Well, I don't know. I, along with every *human being* of course wish that he didn't eat the fruit, but so it was.

However, we have the unlimited grandeur and privilege to call the blessedness of eternity himself, Jesus, the creator, as also the name of our savior.

So I think it more than evens out.

Now, as I said, we are not to know the full picture right now. We must only live lives through *faith and obedience and trust*, before we can be taken back to God.

This is how God ordained it. We have to display trust. We must recircle back, and conquer the things that made us fall. This is by design. That way, we will learn the eternal lesson, and we will *never* sin again after this existence.

I'm more than willing to go through this once, if it means never having to ever, ever go through this again.

Ever and Forever.

This is why Jesus said he wants us to forget about everything else and focus on the Kingdom of God. This is what he meant when he said the birds do not worry for their food or clothes. He wants us to look to his beloved face, and *trust.*

Trust that he will save and raise us from death. From a hard life of pain and suffering, to an eternity that is *unimaginable.*

Picture it my friend. eighty or ninety years of pain, and honestly for many people, even less, in exchange for an eternity of bliss and love.

It doesn't even *compare*.

I know it is hard. I get it. We feel like a lifetime of suffering is more than we can bear, and that it's unfair to ask us to do this. But I assure you, the exchange will be worth it. We have to believe it. I know it's hard, but we have to believe it.

For God will make good on his promise.

Trust me.

If you don't believe or listen to any other words I ever wrote or told you, *believe that.*

Mercy, Evil and Cruelty (To Animals and People)

After Adam was created, God actually brought every single animal to him to name.

Yes, fish are named "fish" because Adam named creatures who swim and breathe underwater as such.

This is not a joke. Adam named all the animals.

Seriously. *All of them.*

Cows, Monkey, Rhino, Giraffe, Lion, Bear, Cat, Dog, Whales, Dolphins, Insects, Bugs, Birds.

All of them.

Do you understand the privilege we were given? Animals are named as such from man.

When God created the animals, he only described them. He called them "Fowl of the Air" and "Creature that walketh the land" and "Creature that swimmeth in the Sea."

He wanted to give Adam the *privilege* of naming them. The privilege to name creatures he did not create.

Amazing.

Now this privilege should not be lost on us, that is, the privilege of taking care of the animals and creatures of this earth. This is because we were put in charge of them.

Why do you feel we have such an urge and responsibility and instinct to take care of them and make sure they don't go *extinct?* Why do you feel we feel such loss at finding out a species no longer exists?

This is not because of nothing. This was by design. It is in-built in us to want to take care of animals and life on this planet.

This is why we do it. Not because of anything else.

Yet, nowadays, as in ages past, we cruelly mistreat animals. *We beat and starve them.* We shoot and kill them with no mercy. We run them over and laugh when they get hit by cars and other forms of violence.

Of course, this is not all people. But so many still do.

We should not feel and behave thus towards the animals placed in our care by God.

For this was a lesson for us to learn to care for living creatures, *a token* to help us begin to understand the tender care God has for us.

This is why animals were created.

After we sinned, God then mercifully gave them to us to consume for food. This was NOT how animals were supposed to be treated. They weren't supposed to be *eaten* for goodness sake.

Do you understand this? They were created to be our friends and companions. Yet they willingly give up themselves to be eaten, as God commanded.

We all should, as many do now, make every effort to better care for animals, who were created to give us comfort and companionship.

The thing is, we care little for our fellow man. We have no problem being cruel to other humans, when they make us mad, or even when they *don't*. We have no problem giving another person "what they deserve" if they did something wrong.

We simply lack mercy.

But should we be like this? No. We should have mercy on people when they do wrong, as well as animals, who cannot talk or defend themselves from human attack. We should show compassion on them for doing things they only know to survive. But how can we begin to show mercy, true mercy to animals, when we do not have mercy on human beings? We mercilessly kill and harm each other.

This is not right. We show ourselves savages that the devil delights in, for he loves to see chaos and acts of brutal vengeance, with no mercy.

We do not have to be like that.

God is unending mercy and infinite love. This is a trait of God. We can be like him.

We can be like him, who does not murder us in a second for doing something wrong, or swat us with a human swatter, or beat us with a broom for running around in the house, and looks at us with mercy and love, even though we sin every day and *often in front of his face*.

Consider this. Are you repulsed by a squirmy centipede? Does a dung beetle make you grimace? Or perhaps, a nasty rat running through garbage repulses you to the point you want to vomit when you see it running through filth and wet trash?

Guess what? We look nastier than that to the Holy, Infinite, Omnipotent One.

We are dirty, disgusting creatures, scurrying around, sifting through dust and garbage on this dirty planet, where everything dies and withers away.

Do you really tell yourself that we look *clean* and spotless in front of God?

No. We are filthy, dirty insects who scurry around like ants when a storm approaches.

Let God get angry at us, and allow natural disasters to happen. Look how we run and cower like the insects that we are.

So why do I speak this harshly? Because I want to drive home the point that we must see animals in a better light. They are to us, as we are to God.

And yet, We are not equivalent to God as to them. *All animals know exactly who God is,* and worship him constantly, on a daily basis, even though they cannot talk.

So first, let us treat our fellow man better. Then it would be a simple matter to treat animals better, for we would extend that same compassion to them as we would to ourselves.

So let us treat animals better. They are a very precious, privileged, tender and *irreplaceable* gift.

A *gift* given to us by the Creator himself.

Time (A little for now, a lot later)

Imagine this.

How long has man been upon the Earth? Biblical teaching tells us that it has only been somewhere between 6000-7000 years. This I personally believe. However, let us, for the sake of argument, protract the currently held scientific belief that the Earth is billions of years old.

You want 10 Billion? Sure. Oh, wait, you meant 15 Billion Years old?

Sure, why not.

Let us say that man has lived and existed on the earth for what? Maybe around a half million of these years? Again, I do not believe this. My beliefs are solely grounded in Bible evidence, which expounds upon the truth of creation and our history as it is showed down through the ages. I believe that man has only existed for somewhere between 6000-7000 years.

But now, back to the currently held scientific arguments.

So, let's take half a million years of man's suffering. Sure. That is five hundred thousand years.

That is a lot of years of suffering no?

I mean, God could not exist, because what God would let man suffer for 500,000 years?

Well, he *wouldn't*. But that's another argument.

As for now, let us imagine and envision the totality of man's suffering for five hundred thousand years. Go on, take a moment to picture it. So very long that time is. Can you imagine the suffering? Surely, we have suffered more than what *should* be fair.

But still, let us hold to the number of five hundred thousand or thereabouts as currently believed.

Now, my dear reader, compare and contrast that with *Infinity*.

Yes. Infinity.

We often try to imagine and quantify the word. We try to put a meaning behind it, to give us an idea of how large it is.

But I am here to tell you, that man, in his current mental state, cannot.

Sure, we can put symbols and mathematic equations against it to symbolize *approaching* infinity, but we can never *quantify* it.

Why? Well, because its infinity.

You know, never-ending. Never ceasing. Never stopping. Imagine starting to count at one, then keep counting for infinity. Or infinity as we perceive it now. Go on, start.

Now keep counting for the space of infinity. Forever. For all time. Forever and ever.

Guess what? By definition, you still haven't counted to infinity. Do you know why? Because infinity, by definition is never-ending. No end, jack. No end in sight.

For all of eternity. Unending. Forever. And Ever.

Yeah.

So why do I ask you to compare and contrast a *mere* five hundred thousand years with infinity?

Well, to show you that whatever amount of human suffering you, as a human determines we as a race has endured, it is nothing to the concept of *infinity and eternity*.

For infinity never ends. Eternity never ceases.

Even if we have collectively gone through pain and suffering as a whole for even the fictional number of five hundred thousand years, (we have not) it is still not equivalent or comes close to the number of infinity, which is not even a *quantifiable* number.

So when you are tempted to feel down, and let the derivatives of the conscious world make you feel existentially disturbed, remember that when we get to heaven, we will live forever.

Yes, forever.

An unending existence. A never-ending consciousness. Immortality. Infinite Immortality.

Forever and Ever and Ever and Ever and Ever and Ever and Ever and Ever and Ever and Ever and Ever and Ever and Ever and Ever and Ever and Ever and Ever and Ever and Ever and...

Do you understand?

Our troubles on this earth, while it seems harsh and long, is not even a drop in the bucket of time. One day, we will look back at these simple early years (as much as God lets us remember) and wonder how we felt one thousand years was long. Or the distance between the Milky Way and Alpha Centauri was so immense.

Those distances will feel like a few inches. Yes, a few inches. *Trust me.*

Infinity awaits us. Do not be misled by the terms of the here and now. *We live for the future.* The future of infinity.

To that, our sufferings are not even sufferings. They are but a small blip of existence we had to live through to get to the goal.

The *goal* of existing in eternity.

Choice (The Universe depends on it)

It's time to get *very* scientific.

By the way, science should not conflict or contradict religion. Neither should religion contradict science.

Science should *complement* religion and vice versa. This is how it should be. However, many do not believe that science is based in religion.

For that, we make a grave mistake.

Science is bounded and wrapped up in religion. God created the world and set the laws of physics, not man.

We ought to respect his *infinite authority* on the subject.

Ok, so back to science.

We determine in our limited understanding of reality and the universe, that there are currently four dimensions. Three of which are bound the X, Y and Z axis's, or in other words, the fundamental three dimensions of existence, the first, second and third dimension, with the fourth dimension being time.

We also appear to accept that Time, the fourth dimension is the constant by which our reality is based, and as such, it is the universal constant, or unbreakable law, as with the speed of light.

But what if I told you that the universal constant was not light, or time, or some other fifth dimension we don't know of, or theoretically suppose?

But that it was simply the all-encompassing, all existential, all involving power of choice?

Yes. Choice.

Not E=MC2. Not 186,000MPH. *Nope.* Not even close.

It is choice. It is the one constant that must by definition be followed, or the Universe would cease to exist.

So what could I possibly mean by this? It's simple, really.

God has determined that the universe will only exist in accordance with choice by every single living creature. A *choice* to serve him and live under his immutable will.

As such, the universe shall continue to spin and expand or do whatever mysterious thing it does that we cannot fathom for now.

So you may claim that you still do not understand.

Well, think of it this way.

God will never allow a universe to exist, in any form, where the creatures do not have a choice to serve him or not.

Yes. It's that simple. God would rather blink all matter and beings out of existence, than have a universe of mindless drones, who serve him out of forced programming.

God has shown that he does not, and will never be pleased with forced or robotic obedience.

Now this is important my friend, for this is what hinges the very fabric of reality itself. If we did not have a choice to serve him, it is essentially not even existence, hence, by definition, God *would not allow* this to occur.

God only takes pleasure in created beings choosing to serve him.

This goes for ALL created beings. The ones in heaven. The ones in other worlds. The ones existing in the other parts of the infinite universe.

It all must be by choice.

Or we do not exist.

Can you begin to understand why the omnipotent God would do things this way? He who has all power and all knowledge, would only be satisfied if intelligent beings and creatures *choose* to serve him.

I am attempting to explain it to you, and it grossly exceeds my understanding as well.

For this is God's territory. Only he understands why he wants it that way.

We can however, understand that he wants it that way in part, to give us freedom. And honestly, I thank God for this. I want to be free to choose to serve the

God of the Universe, knowing that he created me intelligently enough to recognize his Deity and sovereignty.

This actually fills me with joy, as it only further proves that God is fair in all his dealings with men, no, with all created beings. Angels, men and people or beings of other worlds we will only meet when we get to heaven.

Therefore, I am immensely happy to exist in this construct of reality that God has graciously created. Aren't you glad that God is a *good* God? Do you dare envision or imagine the unfathomable eternality of a God who was *not* good? Or *just?* Or *fair?*

A God who only wanted service from blind robots?

You know who wanted that? You guessed it, the devil.

The nerve. Then he even accused God of wanting what he himself wanted. A forced existence. A forced worship and praise by created creatures.

Thank God for himself.

Yes, you heard me right. Thank God for God and his own traits of omniscient fairness and choice.

Thank you Jesus for your unlimited mercy and compassion. Thank you God for your never-ending love and freedom.

The *freedom* to serve you by choice.

Why We Look For The Rainbow

Do you look for the Rainbow after the falling rain? I do. But why? Why do we look for the Rainbow? What's so special about it?

Then, as a matter of query, you may even ask: *"What is a Rainbow exactly?"* and *"Why does it take place?"* Well, science has an explanation of this phenomenon. Well, an explanation of *how* it forms, because *of course* it does. The thing is, I generally accept the premise behind how we believe it is formed.

Photons and/or particles of light, in the form of sunshine, is reflected through billions or trillions of drops of rain, and the light is broken up into its base components or spectrums, as it were commonly referred to as *colors*, and this is what is seen as a bow of colors in the clouds, presenting itself and only seen *after* the rain.

Hence, it is called a *Rain*-bow.

However, while the scientific premise may be acceptable as to attempting to explain how it forms, the reason behind *why* it forms, well, that is something else entirely.

You see, the Rainbow is not of scientific significance only. Rather, once we explain its formation as it appears to us on the Earth, we tend to forget the reason as to why it was actually placed there.

That is, the reason God *put* it there.

For that, we need to travel way back in time. A time of Noah's Ark. A time of the Flood.

The Bible teaches us that long ago, God determined that the wickedness of men had become so great, that he actually regretted creating man. Now if you do not subscribe to such beleifs, then you cannot see why God would regret making man. However, the Biblical record stands, and it is what I believe to be the truth.

God told Noah to build an Ark. He gave him the instructions. He told him how to build it. He gave him the measurements. All blueprints directed from the Creator himself.

And Noah did as God asked. He built the Ark.

We all know the story from there of course. Noah preached for 120 years, then the Flood came. Everyone died. Yes, man and beast. Everyone outside the Ark. Everyone perished except Noah, his wife, and his three sons, and their wives. A total of 8 people. Yes, only 8 people survived the flood, out of all who lived and existed on Earth at the time.

For those who do not believe, I only offer you the record, as it stands, with no intent to argue its validity. I only share with you my belief.

And I do believe.

Now, before we get back to the Rainbow, I would be remissed if I didn't touch a little on Noah. I mean wow, that guy. He really had faith. He literally preached and built, and built and preached. He preached the message of coming destruction by flood for one hundred and twenty long, *long* years.

Can you imagine that? Preaching and shouting a message for one hundred and twenty years? Who does that? Who tells people that a flood is coming that will wipe them all out if they don't believe and join in the Ark to the saving of their lives and souls? We barely live to be one hundred these days. Who would spend their *entire* life just preaching one *singular* message?

Well, *Noah did.* And no, he didn't spend his whole lifespan preaching, but he dedicated over a hundred years just to preaching. He literally preached well over the span of a hundred years.

Now, even if you do believe the Bible doctrine, and subscribe to this teaching, the thought of this whole event and what happened may go over your head. Or perhaps, you may feel as if the amount of time Noah preached was simply a small amount of time, for men in those days lived to be hundreds of years old right?

Nope. It was actually a *very, very long time.* The people who lived back then experiencd time as it flows just like now. Twenty four hours were in a day, as it is now. Weeks, months and years passed, as it does now. The people who lived in the time of Noah had an immense amount of time to seek mercy and forgiveness from God. They had ample time to stop their wickedness and turn back to the right way.

Imagine this for a moment.

Noah preached for one hundred and twenty years. Yes, 120 years. Now imagine as it were, counting back from this very same year, or perhaps the next, being the year 2020-2021.

This means that if we were to apply the same amount of time to the moment Noah began preaching, that would mean that Noah would have begun preaching the message of the flood since 1900.

Yes, the year Nineteen Hundred.

Imagine it. Noah would have started preaching about the coming flood from before many of the events of our modern history. He would have started clearing out a large section of land whereby he could start working. He would then have been right there, working steadily along, as the great hurricane hit Texas, killing over 8000 people. He would still be there, in his place, preaching and building. He would then have witnessed the beginning of the first World War. He would have witnessed countries battle each other, watching thousands die, all while preaching the message of the coming flood.

Noah would have then watched as the Great Depression begun. He would still be right there, preaching the coming flood, now set to come less than a hundred years from then.

He would have watched on still, as after the first brutal world war, and a great depression had passed, the world became embroiled in yet a second World War.

Still, Noah would be there, preaching his message of the coming flood.

Then, as the decades of the 1950's and 60's rolled in, he would still be right where he was, preaching the message of the coming flood, and imploring all who would be saved, to come and join him in the Ark. He would have watched on, as the civil rights era took place, where Black men and women fought for their God-given rights and the right to be treated fairly. He would still be preaching for men to turn away from their wickedness, even as the internet was born.

He would then have continued to preach well into the 1970's and 80's, where we began to worry about yet another war with Russia.

Still yet, he would have continued preaching and building the Ark, which was still far from complete, as he watched the world continue on into the 90's, with pop culture and diversified cultural norms taking off. He would have still been preaching, while we were looking at *Full House, Family Matters* and *The Fresh Prince*.

He would have saw all the trends continue yet, even into the 2000's, as technology boomed. He would still be there, preaching the coming doom on the human race, pleading with all to come to God and save themselves in the Ark.

Yes, even witnessing in horror, Noah would have watched as many perished in the terrible tragedy of 9/11. He would still be there preaching, as Katrina happened. Well into the twenty teens, he would still have been there, preaching the message of the coming inevitable flood.

Finally, even in 2019, he would be there, preaching for all to come to God, for the time was near and the Ark was nearing completion.

Then, as 2020 came in, he would be seen, entering his final pleas to men, after now being there, building and preaching for over one hundred and twenty years.

Do you begin to understand just how looooooong of a time this was? How long Noah, old faithful Noah, was preaching?

Can you begin to grasp the mercy God had on those people back then? He really gave them every opportunity to come and change their ways. Yet, they didn't. They kept up their wicked ways, and never changed, even after all that time Noah preached. Even after one hundred and twenty years. *More than a century* of preaching and pleading.

I hope you can understand just how long a time that was. How long of a time mercy remained for people.

Yet none took it. No one except for Noah and his family.

Now, coming back to my first point, the reason behind the Rainbow, and why we look for it, we then continue on, as we know that the flood took place.

In the flood, all life on Earth perished.

After the flood, Noah faithfully came out of the Ark, and provided an offering to God, a very immense offering of one of each of the clean beasts that resided in the Ark, as a *Thank You* offering to God for saving and sparing them on the tumultuous waters of the great flood.

God saw it, and was pleased with the sacrifice Noah made, and then, in mercy made the wonderful decree that the seasons would continue on, and that time would continue to flow, and that he would never again, destroy the Earth by flood.

As a token of that promise, he promised to take his very own bow, that is, the one that surrounds his throne, and curve it in the clouds and make it visible for man to see *after it rained.*

This was done to remind us of the promise of hope, that he would never destroy us all off the face of the Earth again by flood. We are to look into the clouds after a downpour of rain, and remember the promise given long ago, *that day and night shall not cease.*

Such is our hope. This is why the Rainbow *is* that symbol of hope. We no longer have to fear that we would all be destroyed together off the Earth. We no longer have to worry about a sentinel event that will wipe out the human race.

God promised. We can be sure of that promise.

This is why I am confident that no existential derivative can take place, killing all life on the planet. No such thing will happen. We don't have to fear. We don't have to worry. We have the promise and protection of God.

A God who is good. A God who never, ever breaks his promises.

That's why, after it rains, and I see the sun come out, I always look on the opposite of the sun, on the clouds, to see if I can see the Rainbow.

And it has never failed to show, as long as the sun shines through the rain. It will *always* show.

I know I can always look up and see it, as promised. This gives me *eternal hope*.

When I am feeling down, I always remember that. I remember that God loves us, and always keeps his promises.

That's why we *look for the Rainbow*.

The Binds of Living Faithfully

So you may ask, what does it take to be a true Christian? What do you really have to do to be that *"better"* person.

Well, I could go on an elaborate lecture and tell you this and that.

I could tell you of how to dress, and how to eat, and how to speak, and how to carry yourself, and conduct your affairs.

But that does not make you a *Christian*.

I can tell you to give away your money the poor. I can tell you to go to church. Both would be nice, but even that does not make you a Christian.

I can tell you to read one hundred verses from the Bible a day, and go and preach to the choir, but still, that does not make you a Christian.

So what then? What makes you a Christian? It's simple really.

Your belief in the only begotten of the father, *Jesus Christ.*

That, and that alone, makes you a Christian.

Not your works, or your deeds. Not your friends. Not your many biblical achievements.

Not your many trips to a building we designate to worship in. Not how you dress or the food you eat, or how much money you have.

It is your sole belief in God.

Do you believe in the Almighty? Do you believe in his Son? Do you believe he came to this earth to die for our sins?

This is the fundamental core of being a Christian.

It doesn't matter if you are affiliated with a religion or church. What matters is your heart and faith.

Now, if you truly believe in God and Jesus, you will do the things he asks of you to do. It's that simple. If you do not believe or want to believe, then ultimately, *you won't.*

This is how it goes. You either choose to live the way he asks you to, *or you don't.*

It is important to understand that people often get hung up on labels. To an extent, labels are ok, as long as it does not define your life or your belief in what is right.

Labels are there for our human benefit. We must understand that this does not confer as a specified group with God.

Nope. God does NOT see one group of people in one religion as only those who serve him. This is important to remember, when he says in the Bible that one day, *all his people,* from all over and from many churches all over will come to him.

So we must remember that no one church or religion holds the entirety of God's children.

Not by a longshot.

Now, once you begin to speak on religion and specific groups, you often get the question of how someone should live to define themselves as of the particular religion or faith.

That is, what is the part of religion that makes us live and do good? What makes us into good people?

In other words, what are the *binds of living faithfully?*

Well, for one, you live in such a way as you would want to be treated.

Remember when Jesus said this? He specifically wanted us to know that to live in such a way that would be pleasing to God, you must live and treat your fellow man as *you* would want to be treated.

"Do unto others, as you would have done unto you."

A simple and easy commandment, and one that is easy to follow. You don't want people stealing from you, then *don't steal from people*. Don't want to be lied to? Yup. Don't lie to others.

See? It's really not hard at all.

We often make it way harder than it needs to be. Just live your life in a way that does no harm to others, as you yourself do not wish harm to come to you.

So what else? Well, the Bible also says to *"Do Justly, Love Mercy and Walk with thy God."*

Ok, so we have the "Walk with thy God" part down. We just discussed the "Do Justly" bit of the verse. So all that is left is the "Love Mercy" part.

Ah. There it is.

We need to love mercy. So what does it mean to *"Love Mercy"*?

Well, simply put, love to show kindness and mercy to your fellow man, just as God has mercy on us.

There are many times we can show mercy and we do not. Sure, let the image of a suffering animal come across the TV and we are all in tears, and rightfully so, but yet you walk down the street, and God forbid someone bumps into you by accident and scuffs your brand-new shoes, and you are already planning how to murder them.

Yes, I know this is exaggeration, but it gets my point across. We lack mercy in matters where it is needed most. If we truly loved mercy, many, many bad things would not happen to people. There would be little to no crimes against each other. We would be able to live more *peaceably* with each other.

It is important to remember that the things I discussed above are extremely easy to do. Anyone can do it.

If they choose.

God does not ask of us hard things, or things that are nigh impossible. He is extremely fair with us. He just asks us to live with love in our hearts for people, and not to mistreat and abuse others.

If we were able to do that perfectly, we would be living, essentially, in the lower atmosphere of *Heaven itself*, with but a small step left to carry us over to the true heaven when Jesus comes.

When you think about that, you understand that it is not difficult to live as a Christian, or to live faithfully.

Simply put, *Believe and trust in God, have faith, live in such a way he asks, then live justly, love mercy and continue to walk with him.*

Or in other words, looking to *Jesus and his lovely face.*

That's it. Seriously, *that's it.*

Why do we think that this is so *difficult* to do?

Part III

A Few Religiously Themed Short Stories (Fiction)

"And there are also many other things which Jesus did, the which, if they should be written every one, I suppose that even the world itself could not contain the books that should be written. Amen.

John 21:25 KJV

The Infinity Span

*"Some seek to aspire to fortune and fame. Some, their passions
they fail to tame. But there are those who seek, the simple
encounter of friendship to endeavor, a tale of the man who once
made a friend, a young companion who could live forever."*

P aul had lived by himself now, for a few years,
and he had, after a long time, become used to
taking care of his small woodland ranch, one
that he inherited from his father many years ago. His
father was a strict man, and Paul was raised to be
studious and Christian-like, albeit, he never went to
Church. His family did, and often urged him to go. He
even knew a lot of the Bible himself and made efforts
to live based on its principles, yet somewhat never
truly believing that religion held the key to man's
happiness. This he felt, as he had suffered tragic things
in his past, and because of this, he had become
somewhat disconnected from most things in life.

He was not what you call a man in the throngs of happiness, but he was beginning to appreciate and realize the meaning of peace. This he felt was his life now, and as such, kept away from the public when he could, for he tried to avoid getting to know people too closely. This behavior had a reason of course, and we shall see this reason a little bit later.

As time rolled by, however, Paul became lonely. He no longer liked living by himself, and longed for a family and people around him, and was sad that he had no one to share his time with and to live with.

He was still very much hesitant to interact with people, for he did not want to get to know them personally, but he felt the pangs of loneliness greatly, and many days went by, where he suffered and cried for lack of a family, or a friend, or companion to talk to.

One afternoon, as the man was working towards the corner of his ranch, in a heavily wooded area that connected to a dense woodland beyond his small property, a young boy walked out towards him. He appeared very disheveled, and his clothes appeared to be very old.

The boy was not filthy or covered with dirt, but he did not have on what we refer to as normal clothes, rather, he did not dress as one would dress nowadays, as in the attire of a simple t-shirt and jeans or slacks or something along those lines.

He wore a large button-up shirt, almost two times his proper body size, and the tail of the shirt hung down close to his knees. To keep it from blowing every which way, he tied a thin piece of torn cloth around the center as a belt. He also wore a pair of pants, but it was a loose-fitting pair of cotton slacks that fit him like baggy pants, and it swung and blew in every which way as he walked towards Paul.

Startled, Paul asked the boy where he came from. The boy, stopped and took a good look at Paul and said he was hungry, and asked if Paul could provide him with some sustenance.

"Kind sir, I'm desperately hungry. Do you have sustenance that I may partake?" The boy asked.

"Sustenance?"

Paul answered him, not surprised by the word itself, for he knew what it meant, but surprised that a young boy would use such a word to describe food.

"Yes kind sir. Do you have any for me to partake? If not, I understand."

"Yeah, I have some food at home, but are you lost? How did you get here?" Paul asked.

"I walked kind sir."

"Sure, I can see that, but I mean, are you alone? Did you lose your family? Where are your parents?"

"I don't have any."

"You don't have any parents? Why? Did something happen to them? Do you need help?"

"No, I am ok."

"So why is a young boy walking in the woods by himself…"

"Please kind sir, do you have any sustenance I may partake in?" The young boy asked again. *"I do not*

have any money on me right now, but I can work to earn my meal.”

~Part II~

At repeating this, Paul, stopped questioning the boy and agreed to take him back to the house for some food. He appeared to be hungry, and Paul did not like seeing someone hungry, being denied food. He was still filled with questions to ask, as he was dressed very strange, and spoke even stranger for a young boy, but since the boy did appear hungry, he decided he would feed him, and see if he needed to clean up and use the bathroom to relieve himself, then he would question him some more and find out what happened to him.

As Paul walked next to the boy, the boy walked alongside him and walked with his head straight, like as a man, not as a young boy would do, who upon walking in the woods, would most likely dart his head up and down, back and forth as he looked at the trees and listened to nature. The boy walked as if he was a man, a man, who upon having a task, would be keen to get to his destination, complete his mission, and then get back home. Such is the way the young boy walked. His stride contained a maturity about it that Paul couldn't help but recognize.

At his house, the man took out a bowl, and filled it with some baked macaroni and cheese he had made the night before, and had leftovers in the fridge. The man then heated it in the microwave, and as he did so, the boy, sitting on the floor of the entrance of the kitchen, watched the microwave keenly, and then said the strangest thing:

"I can never truly get over this thing you refer to as technology."

Paul was once again surprised at what the young boy said, but resolved himself to hold in his many questions, as he wanted to ensure the boy had gotten a chance to eat, and he promised himself he would not ask any more questions of the boy until he had at least done that.

As he ate, Paul observed the boy, who, preferring to sit on the ground, ate his food quietly and calmly. He was indeed famished, for he finished the first bowl, then politely asked if it wasn't too much to please have another. Paul answered he had more, and gladly provided a second bowl to the young boy after re-heating it once again in the microwave.

As the boy ate the second bowl, Paul then had the idea that the boy must be homeless, and perhaps a wandering bastard, who knocked about and worked small jobs here and there for his meals. He supposed that the boy was probably a shelter kid, who probably for whatever reason, got away, or perhaps was sent away due to circumstances unknown to him.

He made up his mind that he would try to get to the bottom of this, and began to think of ways to question the boy politely, but directly, hoping he could provide answers to his strange appearance and to the way he spoke, for this was simply not normal. As he got deep in thought, the young boy finished the second bowl, and looked up and spoke to him.

"Thank you kind sir. How much may I pay you for this meal?"

The boy asked.

Pulling him out of his deep thought, Paul, half not sure of what the boy said, and half still surprised at the manner of speech the boy maintained, asked him to repeat his question.

"I only ask if you would tell me how much this meal cost, and I will work to pay you back."

"No, no. You don't have to pay me back. It's completely fine. Would you like something to drink?"

"Yes, I would be in your debt for a cup of water."

"Do you want ice?" Paul asked.

"Oh no, you don't have to attain that level of sophistication for me, a plain cup of plain water is fine."

"No, no. It's no trouble at all. I will get you some cold water from the fridge."

"Ok. Thank you very much."

Paul brought back a tall clear glass of water he poured from a mug he kept in the fridge. The young boy drank it and when he was done, he smiled and handed the glass back to Paul.

"Thank you kind sir. You have done me a great service. I thank God for your kindness."

"Oh, no problem. It was just some mac and cheese and water. You don't have to thank me for that. I was glad to give a hungry kid some food. Oh, by the way, what is your name, son?"

The boy smiled at Paul and asked him if he seemed that young to him.

"Do I appear that young to you, kind sir?"

"Well yeah, you're just a kid. You don't look older than thirteen if I had to guess. Why? Are you older than that?"

The young boy let out a small laugh. He looked at Paul for a second, then said his name was "Nathial"

"Nathial?" Paul asked. *"Is that short for Nathaniel? What is your last name?"*

"Son of Tobias."

"Son of Tobias? Wait, I don't think that is a last name. Isn't that a designation of who you are in a family? As a matter of fact, isn't that how the olden people of the Biblical era referred to themselves?"

"Yes."

"So why do you call yourself that, son? Do you not have a modern last name?" Paul inquired.

"No, I suppose I don't have one." Nathial answered.

"Really? Everyone has a last name. Wait…"

Paul then had the idea that it must be that the boy was indeed a bastard, without a father, who was probably put up for adoption somewhere, and he never knew his proper surname. But then he stopped, for he remembered that even if a child does not take his biological father's name, he still has his birth name from his mother. Paul then looked at Nathial, ready to ask him what his mother's last name was when Nathial began speaking to him.

"What is your name, kind sir?" Nathial asked.

"My name? My name is Paul."

"That is a strong, noble name, Paul. You are named after the great Apostle and Missionary, of the same name, who lived and spread the word of Christianity. This is a good name. I thank you for sharing your name with me. Now, I

know you have a lot of questions you appear to want to inquire of me, but can I beg you, if it is not too much trouble, to let me lay down here on your floor and rest for a little bit. I am immensely tired and could use the rest. I can give you my word, that if you let me rest here for a few moments, when I awake, I shall provide you with all the answers you need."

"Ok, fair enough. I do in fact, have some questions for you, as I wanted to try to see if I could find your caretakers or guardians. But that can wait for a few moments. Go ahead and get some rest, but when you wake up, please tell me the truth. I'll be waiting here."

"Yes kind sir. I promise I will tell you everything."

And with that, the young boy lay down on the floor and went straight to sleep. Paul went to his bedroom and got a small sheet from the closet, and lay the sheet over the young boy as he slept. He watched the boy as he slept, and was amazed at how fast he went to sleep, as well as his comfort in sleeping so easily on the floor. Paul then began to wonder what types of hardship a young boy such as this could have undergone, for he was grateful and quite comfortable sleeping on the floor, when most people nowadays would not be so inclined.

He then shook his head, as he pictured the boy probably sleeping out in the woods at night, homeless and cold by himself, and felt sad that there were people such as this, who suffered so greatly in this life, that a hard floor, after a plain jane meal was comfort enough for him, to be so greatly appreciated.

Paul decided he would stop work for the rest of the afternoon, and stay in the house. The boy still slept comfortably on the floor and appeared peaceful. Paul watched some TV, ate a small dinner, took a shower, and came back to find Nathial still sleeping. He watched the boy, smiling to himself at how familiar to a sleeping child he was, and thus could not bring himself to wake him up. By now it was late, close to nine-o-clock at night. Paul decided wherever the boy came from, it could wait until the morning. He then slipped a small pillow under his head, and then feeling tired himself, went to his room to turn in for the night.

~Part III~

Early the next morning, as Paul got up, he walked over to the area the young boy had fallen asleep and found him sitting on the ground, staring at the bookshelf he had in the corner of the room. He saw Paul and greeted him.

"A Good Morning to you Paul, I thank God for this new day. Thank you for allowing me to rest my body."

"Sure Nathial. Were you up long?"

"I awakened about one hour ago as you would say."

"I would say?" Paul thought to himself.

There he goes, yet again, speaking so strangely for a young boy his age.

"Ok. Do you usually wake up this early? I work here on my ranch, so I get up early to start the day, but it's funny to see such a young boy up so early. Are you hungry Nathial?"

"I would certainly not refuse a small piece of bread, but I wanted to talk to you first as promised."

"No, no. We can eat breakfast first, then we can talk. What kind of host would I be if I made you talk on an empty stomach. We can talk after that, ok?"

"Ok Paul, thank you for your kindness."

Still very not used to hearing a young boy speak this way, but also somewhat happy to have had a young child in his house after so long, he smiled at him and went to prepare breakfast. After a few moments, Paul peeked out of the kitchen and asked Nathial if he needed to use the bathroom.

"Yes, I would like to relieve myself." Nathial answered.

Paul showed Nathial the bathroom, and Nathial walked in, and without closing the door, relieved himself. Paul, seeing that he didn't close the door, closed the door behind him, and waited outside. Once Nathial was done, he came outside and thanked Paul once again for allowing him to use his facilities, then went and sat down in the same place he sat since last night.

After a few moments, Paul finished breakfast and invited Nathial to come to the table to eat. Nathial thanked Paul once again and sat at the table. Paul presented him with a plate of scrambled eggs and toast with butter and a glass of milk. Nathial looked at the plate and asked Paul if he was rich. Paul let out a small laugh but then felt sorry, as he imagined Nathial having a hard life that he couldn't even imagine.

"I can never repay you for this rich meal." Nathial said.

"Don't worry about it. This is all free. I can't imagine what you went through before, but I'm gonna get you help. You can have as much as you like. Please eat. There's more if you want it as well."

Nathial looked at the plate some more, then closed his eyes and cried and thanked God for Paul.

Paul then watched, as the boy cried and prayed. He prayed as a soul who had undergone so much, and lived a brutal life that no one could imagine. Paul began to wonder if Nathial was beaten and starved as a young boy.

After they both ate, Paul invited Nathial to come to the front porch, where they could talk. Paul got a small notepad and a pen, with an idea to write down the young boy's information, and start to find a way to get him back to his family or guardians, or wherever he came from.

Once seated on the bench on the porch, Nathial looked at Paul and begged him to please have an open mind, as he would tell him the full truth. Paul said he would listen and that he could start when he felt comfortable. Nathial began his story.

~Part IV~

*M*y dear friend, did you know how the people of the 12th century dressed? Or have you witnessed species that frolicked back in the early 5th century that are now long extinct? Perchance you know of Beethoven's first girlfriend or Roman Emperor Constantine's love of bananas and passionfruit? I suppose you may answer no to these questions. Indeed, I do not expect you to know the answer to them. However, I only ask you these questions, to tell you that I know. I know that and much more. Much more indeed, for I have witnessed all of it. This will surely sound strange to you, but I assure you, my kind friend, I only speak the truth. I have been around for a very long time. A very long time indeed. I don't wish to startle you my friend, but I vowed to tell you the truth. Even though you see me as a young boy, I am not. I am actually many years old. Not measured by your span of years of common life as a twenty-first-century man, for I possess an infinity span, or what you would refer to as an "endless lifespan". My kind friend Paul, I have walked this earth for many years, and I cannot die, as I am currently immortal."*

Upon hearing this, Paul looked up at Nathial with a puzzled look on his face. Was this young boy playing with him? He looked at him with wondering eyes, trying to figure out if the boy was lying to him, or if he had gone insane. There Nathial was, sitting next to him, speaking to him as no child has ever sounded before, telling him a fantastic thing such as this. Should he believe that this boy, this young boy, was in fact, immortal? Was he some kind of evil spirit in plain disguise? Or perhaps an Angel, who was testing him? No. This simply couldn't be true, because he had watched the boy relieve himself in the bathroom. He had watched him sleep. An Angel should need to do neither of those things.

To make matters worse, Nathial was sitting there, smiling at him. Paul couldn't help but wonder what game was being played on him, and it came out in his response.

"Nathial, why would you lie to me? I felt sorry for you, gave you food, and let you sleep in my house, yet you think it's funny to lie to me? I'm only trying to help you."

"Paul, my dear friend, I promise you on everything I know and hold dear, that I do not lie to you."

"Then why are you smiling? Is this a joke you're playing on me?"

"No my friend. I only smile to make you more comfortable with me. When I have told these things to people in times past, I was afterwards beaten and attacked by cruel men and women, who became angry at me because they felt I was lying to them. This has happened to me countless times. I only smiled to assure you I hold no ill will against you, and I deeply endeavor to promise you, I do not lie to you, my dear kind friend."

"You mean to tell me then, that you are immortal? Then why don't you fight back if you claim people beat you and attacked you? If you are so old and wise, you can defend yourself."

"Sadly I cannot. I am limited only within the body of a young boy as it appears. I can only do what is capable of a young boy, no matter what my mind is capable of. As such, I need occasional sustenance and care, and I possess the strength of but a young boy of twelve. In addition to this, I, unfortunately, need to sleep and rest a little more than

common young boys, for I push my immature body, close to its limits every day."

"Nathial, you can't possibly expect me to believe you, right? No one is immortal. What are you playing at?"

"I assure you, Paul, I am."

"Then can you prove it?" Paul asked. *"Show me something to prove you are immortal."*

As they talked, the breeze picked up a little and blew in their direction, and the sun came out from hiding amongst the clouds and shone on the land. Nathial looked up at the sky and closed his eyes for a moment, then opened them after a few seconds. He began again.

"How can I prove such a thing as immortality to you my kind friend? I only have my true word to give you, and I know that it may not be enough evidence, but what I can tell you, is that I stood and watched the evil King Herod get consumed by worms and die. I watched on as Nero let Rome burn. I studied the actual written teachings and discoveries of Galileo Galilei. I perused the claims of Isaac Newton, and watched on, as symphonies were written by Mozart and

Sibelius. I watched on sadly, as America dropped the first atomic bombs of death on Japan. I cannot make you believe me, my friend, but what I can tell you, is that I have lived a long time, and as such, you may ask me anything of the past two-thousand years that you would like to know, and I shall give you the answer."

These words appeared to convince Paul a little, for they were striking in their delivery, but he quickly brushed it off and decided that the boy must be telling lies, for there was simply no way any of this was true.

"So what then? You're telling me you are all alone? You don't have any family?"

"Well, none alive. They died thousands of years ago."

"Ok Nathial. Say I believe you, how old are you now?"

"I was born in 10 BC in a small dwelling of merchants traveling through Egypt. My family originally lived in Babylon, or Iraq as it is called now."

"Iraq? sure, ok. And…10 BC…wait, 10 BC? As in, "Before Christ?" What?" Paul shouted.

"Yes, my friend."

"Wait, so that would make you…wait how do you count BC years?"

"You count backwards my friend. Then at BC year zero, you count the years forward. So we are now in Anno Domini two thousand and twenty or AD 2020."

"So…wait, you mean to tell me you are over two thousand years old?!?!" Paul shouted out again.

"Two thousand and thirty years old to be exact." Nathial stated.

"No. No. This isn't true. You can't be. No one is immortal. How are you immortal?"

"I was given this gift when I was just twelve years of age. I had a bright dream, with someone telling me I would not die for many, many years, and when I awoke from that point, I possessed an infinity span."

"How did you know if you didn't die right away? How did you know this since back then?"

"At first, I didn't know, but as five, then eight years passed, and my body did not change, despite my mother and father getting older, along with my brothers and sisters as

they grew, I knew what was told to me was right. I knew then, that I could not die. My mother and father at first thought I was of mutated genes, and thus, due to this, I did not grow anymore, but we all soon realized, as my mind and mental capacity grew, but my body did not, that it was not simple physical birth deformities. My parents were getting older, and this was not striking, but to see my older siblings, now grown men and women, walking around, whilst I stayed as a young boy proved to be quite a spectacle and a great wonder to all who knew me."

~Part V~

*S*o what happened?" Paul asked, now becoming more curious about Nathial's story.

"My family did not know what was happening to me, but I knew. I decided that it was best to keep the truth from them, as they would not understand, or would instead claim some evil or supernatural event took place."

"So you hid it from everyone? You did that until all your family died?"

"It was wise because they might have turned on me, as the people I knew and grew up with. Seeing me still walk around as a boy, as they were now elderly, people immediately accused me of evil origin and drove me out of my home. I am not evil, neither have I done anything to show this character, yet people accused and beat me and chased me away. It has sometimes been very hard for me. I have starved and suffered and went many, many days without food and shelter. At times, I begged God to show me the meaning of all of this, but even now, I still do not fully understand my purpose. All I can tell you is that God

has helped me and carried me through all this time, so he must have a special purpose for me."

"Ok Nathial. I don't understand what you're saying, but either way, I need to get you back to where you were. Where did you come from?"

"I don't have a set place to lay my head. I have been wandering all over, working off my meals and shelter wherever I could find it, and sometimes, being blessed to stay with kind souls, who took me in and I spent time with them, until they too, got too old, and passed on. I then became a wanderer again. This is how I have spent all my time living."

"But wait, if you know so much, couldn't you have gotten rich or something with all your knowledge? Like you could share your knowledge with museums and places that value historical knowledge. You could write books and make money and live well. Why not do that?"

"And who my friend, would believe a child wrote an immensely detailed concordance with historical details and facts hitherto unproven to the world? Would they honor a child or a young boy to riches? No. They would never believe

me. In addition to this, I never ascribed to gaining for myself treasures of gold or silver, as I feel that it is ultimately worthless in the face of time. Thus I only work for what I need, with whoever shall accept me, and I continue my journey, careful never to do anything to harm or enrich myself as I traverse the vaults of this new age."

Paul sat there next to Nathial, listening quietly, but very surprised and amazed even now, for he had never in all his life heard a young boy speak like this.

"I don't know Nathial. This is all too hard to believe. Do you mean to tell me that you don't have anywhere to go? So if you couldn't stay here, where would you go?

"Back to wandering, my friend."

Paul thought about it for a little bit. He had listened to the most unbelievable story, yet there the young boy sat, looking at him directly in the eye, showing no nonverbal signs of lying or telling a false or made-up story. Paul still did not believe him, but for some reason, he knew whether for good or bad, this is what the young boy believed.

"So you really have no place to go if you leave here?"

"Yes my friend, I will return to wandering. But I thank you for your kindness to me so far. You have done what many have not. You have listened to me, and given me a chance to peacefully tell you my story. I have not been hit or slapped by cruel men, who think me a liar. For that alone, I thank you. If I must go on my way, I shall go in peace. I thank y…"

"Well, wait a minute Nathial. If you don't have a place to go, and you are telling the truth, then you could stay with me. I mean, I don't have much but…"

Nathial's eyes lit up. He began to smile even more.

"Is this true what you speak, my dear friend? Would you do something so kind such as allow me to stay with you?

"I suppose. I mean, you don't have anywhere to stay right? Plus I couldn't send a young boy on his own to fend for himself out here. It's simply too dangerous. Plus there are a lot of molesters and people up to no good. If you run across one, you won't be able to fight back and defend yourself right?"

"No, my friend, I would be helpless against them, but I have been spared by God's good graces, and now I have been blessed! I can truly stay with you?"

"Yeah, I mean, you aren't bad company."

In all honesty, Paul was lonely, and he thought that it would be good to have a young boy to keep his company every day. Plus if he was as old and wise as he said, he could help out around the house with issues unrelated to physical strength, and if nothing else, his stories could provide entertainment at least, for him.

He still didn't fully believe Nathial, despite his convincing and spectacular words, but Paul figured that until the boy came to his senses, or perhaps he gathered enough info to find his family, he would let him stay, and take care of him. At least until he could be safely returned to his parents or guardians, for Paul still felt, that somewhere out there, his mother or perhaps his father was looking for their lost son.

Nathial stood up and let out a shout, and thanked God for helping him to find such a kind soul to stay with, and he immediately asked Paul what he should be assigned to do, to help out.

"Well, I can't think of anything right now, but for now, you can accompany me wherever I go and stay with me."

"Of course my friend, I shall follow you wherever you want me to go. I will be here for you always."

~Part VI~

For the rest of the day, Paul and Nathial talked, and he spoke of many strange and unknown things to Paul, who amazed at many times, inquired more and more until before they knew it, they had been conversing for hours. Nathial spoke of many things, and many times, taught Paul several things he never knew or even wondered about. This went on for many days, and during this time, Paul had slowly and surely forgotten his past feelings of loneliness, or his plan to return Nathial to his home and guardians. The two became very close and good friends and mostly went everywhere together.

People and neighbors, when they would see them walking side by side, would say hello to Paul and his son, for Nathial had become known to the neighbors and people around them as a son he kept home. To hide Nathial's true intelligence, Paul prepared a story to satisfy everyone who inquired, that Nathial was adopted from a troubled home, and as such, he was home-schooled to keep him away from poor influences that might otherwise further corrupt his mind.

As for Paul, he had now completely forgotten about the plan to find Nathial's true parents or guardians, for he began to get used to having the companionship of Nathial, and even began to love him closely as a friend and companion, and didn't want him to leave.

As time continued on, Paul and Nathial lived well together and took care of one another. Nathial spent every waking moment he could with Paul, and Paul, happy to not be lonely again, trusted and loved Nathial as a close friend.

~Part VII~

A few more years passed, and Paul began to notice that Nathial's body never changed. They had been together now for a few years, and yet he was still the young boy he appeared as, when he first saw him walk out of the woods. Over the years, Nathial reminded him of this, but it wasn't until he began to see it for himself, that it began to appear strange. He thought back to their first conversation when Nathial told him he was immortal and possessed an eternal lifespan, and began to wonder if what Nathial first told him was right.

After many years together, Paul woke up one day sick with a fever. It was mid-summer, and Paul had probably caught something from working around the ranch. He had come down with a bad infection and did not get better, even after a few hours of taking over the counter medicines. As such, as the afternoon wore on and Paul appeared to get worse, Nathial suggested that they go to the hospital.

Once at the hospital, Nathial gave precise, in-depth instructions and health information about Paul to the doctors and nurses, much to the amazement of the medical staff who took care of him, for Nathial was to them, but a young boy of twelve, conversing with medical professionals and using terms he simply should not know. They marveled at how smart he was and told Paul he was lucky to have such a smart and noble son.

"They say you are a good son."

Paul joked, slightly delirious from the medications he received in the emergency room.

Nathial laughed.

That night, as Paul lay in his hospital bed, as the antibiotics and medications slowly infused into his veins, he looked across the room, to see Nathial, sitting in the corner chair, sound asleep, as he had exhausted himself helping Paul get up out of bed and get ready, helped him pack his things, and slowly walked by his side to the car, and helped him drive slowly to the hospital. He had then sat with him and waited, as he was taken in, and cared for. He then did not rest until they had been brought up to the room and settled in. It was now getting late. Paul realized that Nathial, although having the mind to take care of him, had probably pushed himself to the limit, helping to lift him up out of bed, and helping to clean him up, and then carrying his bag and taking care of him until they got to the room. He was probably exhausted in his young body.

Paul then looked at Nathial's face, and noticed again, his unchanged face and body. Perhaps it was the low lighting of the hospital room, or perhaps the effect of the drugs in his system, or perhaps it was the mental association of a hospital with man's mortality, but at that time, it finally hit Paul. Nathial was not normal. This didn't seem right. It had been many years that he had spent with Nathial, yet he seemed to have not aged one day.

Paul had gotten used to Nathial over the years, so it didn't altogether occur to him that Nathial's body did not change. He did not fully realize that he was the one that was getting older. He had started to show quite a few grey hairs on his head and beard, albeit he wasn't up there in age, and had just turned sixty-five the year prior, but he was no longer a young, strong man anymore.

Paul looked at Nathial some more, and finally, after all the time they spent together, he finally realized that somehow, Nathial had not lied to him, and was telling him the truth all these years. Nathial was somehow miraculously immortal, just as he had always said. Paul lay back in bed and began to think about things. His mind wandered to all sorts of topics, and just before he went to sleep, he told himself he would talk to Nathial in the morning.

~Part VIII~

In the morning, as Paul woke up, he was greeted by Nathial and a nurse, who had come to his room to take his vital signs. He was beginning to show improvement, and the nurse told them that the doctor would be by to talk to them later in the day. She then told him that he would get one more course of antibiotics to make sure the infection he had was completely gone. Nathial smiled at the nurse and thanked her for her kind care, and the nurse bent down and kissed Nathial's forehead and said he was so smart and cute, and that Paul was so lucky to have such a caring son.

"Such a sweet child," Nathial said to Paul. *"She reminds me of my sister and her kindness to me a long time ago."*

"If only she knew she was kissing someone who could be her great, great, great, great, great gran...you know what, nevermind."

Nathial laughed at Paul's joke. He always laughed when Paul made jokes about how old he was. He felt it was their very own personal joke, and he cherished it greatly.

"How are you feeling my friend?" Nathial asked.

"I feel better. Thank you my friend for taking care of me. I didn't think I needed to come to the hospital, so I don't know how sick I could have gotten if I didn't come. Thank you for suggesting we come.

"It was my honor, my friend. I would do it for you, anytime and always. I am just glad you are feeling better."

"Yeah, I really needed the medicine."

"Yes, indeed. I simply cannot get over the marvels of modern medicine. I have now witnessed its immense uses, but it still is a wonder to see it work. I only wish such things existed in the olden times."

"I know. I can imagine many, many people could have been saved."

"Yes my friend, but alas, it is God's will, and so it is. I am just glad you are feeling better."

"Yes I am, but Nathial, speaking of God's will, I wanted to ask you something."

"Sure, anything my friend."

"After all this time, do you still not know what your purpose is? I mean, after all the years you have walked the earth?"

"This is strange for you to ask this now, my friend."

"I know, I know, but listen, it finally hit me last night when we got to the hospital room, that you were…telling me the truth all these years. I don't know, but it just suddenly hit me that you are indeed immortal and that you will…"

"Will what my friend?"

"You know what? It's nothing. I apologize for talking so strangely."

"No my friend, you know you can ask me anything."

"Well, it's just that…I don't know…it feels strange to say…"

"Come, tell me, my friend."

"It's just that it just occurred to me, that you will outlive me."

"Oh, I see." Nathial replied.

"Yeah, but of course you would. I can't believe I'm saying this, but I see that you are indeed immortal."

Paul and Nathial both stopped talking and got silent for a moment.

"Yes, my friend, I do not know how long I will walk into the future, but one day, you will grow old and pass away. It is the lot of every man to die."

"I know. It's just sad to think about."

"I know my friend, I know."

They stopped speaking for a while again. Then finally, Paul broke the silence.

"Nathial, I never asked you this, but you always prayed and confessed your love and thanks to God. Is God really real? Is Jesus real?"

"Yes, my friend."

"Wait, yes?"

"Yes." Nathial smiled.

"Really? I mean, was it God who spoke to you in your dream a long time ago? It was God that granted you an unlimited lifespan?"

Nathial looked at Paul for a moment. Paul appeared immensely curious, and stared at him, truly wanting to know the answer. Nathial walked over to the side of the bed and put his hand over Paul's hand.

"Do you remember my friend, at what age, I had the dream when I was told I would have a limitless lifespan?

"Yeah, you said you were twelve right?"

"Yes. Now, let me tell you something that people do not know. Do you know the year and time of Jesus' birth?"

"No, tell me."

"It was actually April of AD 1. Jesus had been born the same year I was going to become twelve."

"Wait, what? So did you see the baby in the manger? Did you see Mary mother of God? Joseph? The three wise men? The Gold, The Frankincense, and The Myrrh? Were you a shepherd in the fields as they watched at night? My friend,

did you see the star as it was in the sky? Wait…wasn't it cold? Wait…no, you said April? It wasn't wintertime?"

Nathial laughed.

"So many questions my friend! I think you are indeed feeling better. I am happy. No, I didn't witness the "nativity" scene, as it is referred to as nowadays. I had only heard of stories of the baby born in the east. I was still in Egypt at the time with my family. Oh, and yes, Jesus was not born on the day we commonly celebrate as Christmas, he was born in the Spring of AD 1."

"Wow. So Christmas is not the day of Christ's birth?

"No my friend, the holiday was derived from a different holiday that was co-opted into the Christian faith by a "melding" of religious beliefs, so to speak, but we can talk about that another time. The reason I told you this, is because I wanted you to know that Jesus is real. I was not there when he was born, but I did talk and speak to him."

"You did? Wow. Seriously?"

"Yes. As a boy. I was at the time seventeen, well, in my mind, because my body was still twelve of course, when my

family had relocated to Nazareth, to live and trade there. We spent several years there, and during that time, I saw and played with him."

"What? My friend, please do not lie to me. Did you really play with Jesus as a young boy?"

"Yes, I did. I would never lie to you, my dear friend."

"Ok, but how was he? Did he tell you he was God? I mean, how did he sound like?"

"Well, he sounded like a typical young boy, growing up and living in the area. He was always lively and spry. He was always a happy kid, and never once got into trouble. I personally never saw him sad to the point where he was despondent, and he always played happily and fairly with kids his age and younger. Sometimes, older kids bullied him, but he never stopped smiling. At times, they did make him cry, but it was like he was fine the very next moment, playing with them and running around as if nothing happened."

"Wow, Nathial. You never told me this before."

"Well, you never asked, my dear friend."

"Please, tell me all about it. What was he like? Did he tell you he was God?"

"No, he never talked about anything like that as a boy. He was seemingly just a simple young boy. He never spoke of God or anything intense or serious, unless a boy was bullying another child, and then he would walk up to the boy and quote old testament verses that said that you should love and take care of your neighbor. The thing is, it never came off pretentious, and for whatever reason, the boy who bullied the child would apologize and stop. At the time, I thought he was just a bit of an overly-studious boy."

"Wow."

"You say "wow" a lot today my friend."

"Well, this is stuff no one knows about right? It's just amazing to hear."

"Well, he always spoke kindly and smiled a lot. He loved people. He would always look around at people like they were so wonderful. He laughed and played and always seemed very happy. My family eventually moved back to Egypt, and I didn't see him any more of course. It wasn't until I saw him many years later, as he was traveling

around, and a crowd was following him everywhere as he preached, did I realize it was him."

"So did you speak to him again?"

"Well, not really. I was in the crowd, walking with my sister and brother, when he stopped, and turned around in my direction, and spoke. I will never forget what he said."

"What did he say?"

"Well, it looked like he was preaching to the crowd, but when he spoke, it seemed as if he was looking at us. The exact words he said were: "My Father has a purpose for everyone, so you must keep the faith and believe. Only through me, by the will of my Father, can you truly have eternal life. Believe in him, and believe in me." When he said that, something hit me in my heart, and he turned around and kept walking."

"So do you think he was talking to you directly? Since he knew you were given the gift of immortality?"

"At the time, I felt the words were important, and I never forgot them, but remember, I had only been twelve for just five years, and I didn't know if I truly possessed an infinity

span. I also didn't fully understand what his words meant, until long after, and many years of walking alone. He wanted me to know that I was given this gift for a reason and that despite my constant hardships, I should keep the faith and believe."

"Wow, I simply cannot believe all that I'm hearing my friend. What an amazing thing that Jesus was talking directly to you."

"Well, he spoke to many, many people directly. Remember, he was a man, walking around, preaching to people, and yes, of course, performing miracles. I did not see one directly with my own eye, perhaps I wasn't meant to, but I knew of people who have been healed by him. People who were never mentioned by name in the Bible, but of course the Bible couldn't contain all Jesus ever did. It would be too much to write about. In fact, I think one of the disciples said just that in one of their books."

~Part IX~

*S*o Nathial, what about the crucifixion? Did you witness that?"

"No my friend, but I heard stories at the time at how terrifying it was. I did experience the earthquake. It was an earthquake that shook the whole world. The sky got dark at bright noon. Everyone felt it wherever they were. That was a terrible, dark day. At the time, in my then mind, I was in my forties, yet as in a boy's body, I still trembled, along with everyone I knew. It was a fearful day. It was the day they crucified the Son of God. Yes, my friend, Jesus is real. God is real."

"I can only say, wow."

"Wow indeed."

Just then, the nurse and aide came back into the room. They brought Paul his morning medicine pills to swallow, along with his breakfast. Nathial and Paul had been talking for a while now and didn't realize the time was passing. Such were their conversations, when Nathial had begun to speak about things of time immemorial.

After the nurse and aide left, they began to talk once more. Paul looked at Nathial and smiled.

"So Nathial, my long-time friend, a man immortal, who has traversed the hallways of time, and played with Jesus, the Son of God as a boy, is standing in my room, a companion to me, a nobody, who like all other men, who must die."

"You are not a "nobody" Paul. You are my dear friend, whom I cherish very much."

Paul looked at Nathial, once again, forgetting his familiarity with him, and seeing once again, a young boy, as he spoke to him about the deep, hidden issues in life, and of details of the past that would be surprising, even to the most learned men in this present day.

"But my friend, it is sad that one day I will die, and you will be alone again."

Nathial looked at Paul and didn't answer right away. He beckoned to Paul to eat his breakfast before they talked more. Paul invited Nathial to share in a bite of food so he wouldn't be hungry, and Nathial reluctantly agreed. After they finished the small meal, Nathial brought the chair in the corner of the room closer to Paul and sat in it.

"Paul my friend. There is something I want to share with you. You have become a close friend of mine, whom I love very much. You are to me, as a dear brother, and as such, I want to tell you something important."

"What is it, my friend?"

"You do not have to worry about leaving me alone."

"Of course I worry about that, my friend. You will lose a friend once again, and who knows who will take you in again. Maybe not for a long time."

"No, no, I mean, you don't have to worry about leaving me alone, because…you don't have to die."

"I don't have to die? Nathial, what do you mean by that? I can't live forever, and I don't possess an unending lifespan. How can I keep living?"

"You can live on as long as I share my gift with you."

"How? Wait, you have the power to share your immortality with others? Nathial, why haven't you shared this with the

world? Or at least with your family? You could have had your mother and father. Or your siblings. Why would you keep that to yourself?"

"I didn't keep it to myself. There were a few select people in the past two thousand years, whom I have shared my gift with. They were close people to me, people who I came to know very closely, and endearingly. I shared my gift with them, but as time went on, they chose to give it back, as they didn't want to keep living."

"So you can share your gift, and take it back if the person doesn't want to live anymore, allowing them to die?"

"Yes."

"I see. Tell me, who has lived the longest with you?"

"Well, since the early nine hundred's. there hasn't been anyone who chose to live beyond two hundred years."

"Why?" Paul asked.

Nathial looked at Paul for a moment, then closed his eyes. After a few moments, he began speaking again still, with his eyes closed.

"*Many men think that being unable to die is a gift. Many wish they had such an ability that they could have and share with their loved ones. Many seek to attain the "fountain of youth" as it is called nowadays, but many do not realize the mental and physical strain it carries with it, nor do they fathom, the toll it takes on your happiness, as you see time and time again, that your loved ones will grow old, become sick and die without you. Man, in his mental state, especially now, is wholly unequipped to deal with the mental rigors and pangs of anguish at being unable to die. Further, they cannot handle the immense recognition of the imperfect state of man itself, as we grow weaker and weaker in squalor. Of the people whom I have shared my gift with, they have eventually, through mental sadness and grief, chosen to give up the gift of an eternal lifespan. This is by design I feel, for man simply cannot live forever, not in this mortal weakened state.*"

"*I see. Then tell me, Nathial, who was the last companion you had, and how long did they choose to live with you?*

"*My last long-time companion was also a man, who very much like you was kind and very friendly. He came to know me as I worked in a small vineyard, in a village outside Paris, around 1500 AD. We became good friends, and he and I often talked of artful things and dreams of his forefathers. He was a simple, yet noble man, and often questioned me a lot about religion, just like you. Before I met him, he had a son, who had died of what we now know as cancer, although at the time, we did not know it. The little boy wasted away in his bed, with bleeding sores all over his body. After I met him, we spent some time together, and I shared my gift with him, for a period from AD 1510 to AD 1690, a total of one hundred and eighty years. It was a wonderful time for us, and we spent many years together, in companionship as father and son in appearances. I taught him many great things of the past, and he often wrote it all down in his journal. It has been many years now, but I deeply miss him."*

"So why did he choose to give up the gift of prolonged life?"

"He had come to miss the face of his son, who had died many years ago. The more the man learned of religion and of God, he became more and more despondent of this life, and longed to die, to one day see his son again. He felt that for every day he was alive, it was a day prolonged upon which he could not see his son."

At this, Paul became quiet, and looked away, with his face in the direction of the window, looking outside. Nathial asked him what was wrong.

"Nothing, my friend."

~Part X~

A short time later, the doctor came into the room and spoke to Paul and Nathial. He assured Paul that since he was doing much better, there was no reason to keep him in the hospital bed, and he could go home, and continue his antibiotic regimen at home in tablet form, and gave him directions to take his pills as instructed. Later that afternoon, Paul was discharged home.

After a few more days, Paul was strong enough to go back to working in the small garden they had planted together, and they both went outside to work with the cucumber vines and the tomatoes. Paul would drive in tall sticks into the ground, and Nathial would prop up the tomato trees and guide the cucumber vines.

As Paul began to work, Nathial could see that he was no longer the strong man he once was, working all day on the ranch as he once did. He observed as Paul stopped to catch his breath a few times. He thought about it and knew that it would be now or never, and as such, he would try to convince his friend to accept the gift he would give him, and prolong his life. This Nathial wanted, for he loved Paul very much, and wished to stay with him for as long as possible.

Nathial began to bring up the conversation once more.

"My dearest friend, I wanted to ask you if you thought about what we talked about while you were in the hospital."

Paul stopped working, and walked over to the front porch, and sat down to rest for a bit.

"Yes, as a matter of fact, I have, Nathial. I wanted to ask you before I gave you an important answer like that, to tell me. Tell me what has been your experience these last two thousand years. Besides your wonderful experiences with seeing and knowing Jesus, what has it been like? What have you seen? Please tell me the truth, my friend."

"My dear friend, you ask me to expound to you the sum of my prolonged life, from a child to now?"

"Yes, Nathial. Please tell me."

"Well, my friend, I have seen and experienced extraordinary things. Things of good and of bad. If I had to list the bad, I would not be honest if I didn't recount to you, experiences of death, violence, murder, war, starvation, sickness, and pain. But if I shall share with you the good, I can recount experiences of joy, happiness, comfort, redemption, love, beauty, and hope. All these things have been intermingled with each other, but despite the bad experiences I had, the good ones far overshadowed the bad ones. The bad times, however, did often come, and sometimes, they did last a long time, as you know such is, the lot of men."

"I see." Paul answered. *"Let me think about it a little more, and I will answer you by the end of the day."*

"Ok, my friend. Please take your time, for this is a decision that must be made with great seriousness and deep ponderance."

The two continued their work in the garden for the remainder of the day, till about mid-afternoon. Upon finishing up, Paul told Nathial that they had done enough for the day, and could continue tomorrow.

They both went inside to prepare dinner, and after eating, they both sat outside once more, watching the sun go down.

"Nathial."

"Yes, my friend?"

"I have something to tell you."

"Anything you want to tell me, you can."

"Well first, I want to tell you that I am sorry, my dear friend, as this is something I kept from you and did not tell you this fact about me for many years. I once was married, and I had a beautiful little girl."

"You did, my friend?"

"Yeah. I was a young father, and I married my sweetheart wife who I knew from high school. Before my father gave me this ranch, we were living together in another part of the area, but after he passed away, I came to live in this small house with my wife and our lovely daughter. We didn't have a whole lot of money, but the ranch did well, and we were ok. We were happy."

"That sounds very wonderful. But tell me, what happened? Did they die?"

"Yes. In a horrible accident. My wife was driving with our daughter in the back seat, and a drunk driver was speeding down the road and swerved on them. My wife panicked and swerved away, but he still hit them, and she lost control of the car and they went over a ravine. The car overturned many times and landed on jagged rocks many feet below. The car didn't burst into flames, but by the time the rescuers got to them, they had both died. My wife and daughter both from broken necks and severe blunt force injuries."

"Oh my dear friend, I am truly sorry to hear this. I wish I had known."

"No, it was my fault for not telling you. I was sad and heartbroken for a few years after it happened, and shut myself away, here on the ranch, and didn't interact with anyone unless I had to."

"Of course. That is understandable my friend."

"After a few years, I was still heartbroken, but above all, I was very lonely. I was so lonely."

Paul began to cry. Nathial put his hand on Paul's hand, and for a moment, they both sat there and cried together. After a few quiet moments, Paul began to speak again.

"But then, when I was at my darkest point in loneliness, you came. You walked out of those woods with your old shirt, and your baggy pants, and came into my life as a companion and friend. By the way, where on this earth did you even get those sorry-looking clothes man?"

Paul and Nathial laughed. They were exceptionally close friends now, and their hearts had intertwined, and they truly cared solely for the other's well-being. If one was sad, the other was too. If one was happy, so felt the other one.

~Part XI~

The sun was setting in the west, and as the last gleams of sunlight began to turn the sky a nice auburn red-orange, they began to talk once more.

"*Nathial, how do you share this gift with another person anyway? Do I have to drink your blood to gain the gift of immortality? Paul asked.*

"*No. no, my friend, I just have to shake your hand.*"

"*That's it? No crazy ritual or something?*"

"*Why do you think that my friend, are you some evil blood drinker? Did you also hide this from me, my friend?*"

Nathial joked with him.

"*Ha. I thought it would be some kind of meaningful ceremony or something.*"

"*No, no, my friend, just a simple handshake. I have to want to share it with you, and the person need only accept the gift, then you can have it. That's it.*"

"*Oh, ok. But wait, how did you know you could do that?*"

"Well, do you remember the bright dream I had when I was twelve? In it, the person told me that I would not die until my purpose was fulfilled, but that I could choose a companion I felt was worthy to walk with me so that my existence would not be lonely and desolate. The gift was intended for perhaps a close family member or friend, or perhaps to a girl I loved, and wanted her to stay with me. Being that I was twelve, I think God meant me more to share it with someone whom I could become friends with, and have a companion to walk with for as long as he deemed I should be alive."

"Did you not love anyone? Like another girl?"

"Oh yes my friend, I had deep infatuations with many women, whom I felt I truly loved, but as I matured in mind, I realized that a girl of my age or slightly older would not be able to keep up with me mentally, and as such, I began to abandon the physical love of a woman, and sought only the companionship of the mind, whether it be man or woman, I would only care about truly getting to know a person's character, and never again to seek any sort of physical gratification."

"So you're a monk then. A two-thousand-year-old monk."

Nathial laughed again. He was always delighted at Paul's age jokes.

"I suppose so, my friend!"

The sun had now altogether set. Paul finally answered the question.

"Nathial, I have thought about it, and I don't think I shall accept your precious gift."

~Part XII~

Slightly saddened to hear this, Nathial asked his dear friend how he came to his decision.

"I think, like your old friend who you once lived with in Paris, I too, long to see my family again."

"I understand my friend."

"Now, it isn't that I don't want to spend more time with you. You have allowed me to be happy once more, and not to feel lonely after my wife and daughter's passing. I will be forever grateful for that. I also don't think I could have asked for a wiser friend, whom I could carry on deep conversations about religion and life, just as you once did with your olden friend. I asked you earlier, what you have experienced in your time, since you were alive, and you told me honestly what you went through. While I can only look forward to many more years of companionship with you, I don't want to see what this world will look like in another fifty or a hundred years from now. This brief life I've lived has been more than enough for me. Especially so, since I have had the rare opportunity to meet and befriend such a noble and trustworthy companion, who has taught me

things I could never have imagined. Now, I only want to live the remainder of my life, then die, for I deeply miss my wife and daughter. I know that one day, in the resurrection, I will see them again. You have been my companion for many years now, and I feel that God has sent you to me, to keep me company and be my friend, but I too, want to die one day, not right now, but one day, in hopes that I will see my family again. The longer I'm alive, the longer I'm delayed from this. When I die, I won't know anything, and the next thing I know, it will be a wonderful reunion with my wife and daughter, and even you, my good friend."

Nathial listened quietly as Paul spoke. He was saddened that one day, he would again lose a valuable friend and companion, but accepted the reason Paul gave, for it was the same reason people have chosen to die over the many centuries he had been alive, albeit Paul was the very first to deny the gift from the onset.

"Paul my friend, I simply don't want to part with your friendship, but I understand your reasons. I will respect them to the utmost."

"Thank you, my friend. I very much enjoyed our time together as well, but I choose to only live for as many more years that I have left, then die, knowing that the next time I open my eyes, I will see my family again. If that means dying sooner, then I will happily go, for I can skip time, and get to the end. After all, isn't that what death is? Essentially a time skip."

"I suppose you could see it that way, my friend. It is your unique way of seeing things that I will miss most when you are gone."

"Thank you, my friend. Coming from a man with an infinite lifespan, that means a lot."

"Well, I mean it. In the meantime, let's go inside, shall we? I want to watch this "game of the playoff" you keep telling me about."

"Game of the playoff? Seriously Nathial?"

Nathial laughed.

"I'm just joking my dear friend. I know it's just called "The Playoffs". I knew you would get all mad if I acted like I didn't know what a modern game looked like."

"Ha, ha. That's why your favorite team will lose."

"I don't think so, they have a strongly built fellow, with a very high jump.

"Well, if his team loses, we can watch another game together."

"Sure my friend. Together and always."

~Part XIII~

Paul and Nathial continued to live together for a few more years, and before they knew it, fifteen more years had passed, and Paul was now eighty years old. Nathial had to help him do many things in the house, and they ended up having to hire a live-in aide, who helped do the things Nathial could not do, as he remained within the body of a twelve-year-old boy. The live-in aide helped cook, clean, and wash, but the most private things, like cleaning him up and washing him when he was too sick to stand, was done by Nathial himself.

One day, as Paul was walking with his cane outside, he collapsed. Nathial was away, at the local store with the live-in aide, buying small groceries they needed. Upon their return, they found Paul laying on the grass in the front of the yard. Nathial ran to him as the live-in aide called the ambulance for help. Before the ambulance could arrive, Nathial held Paul's hand and asked him if it was time. Paul shook his head weakly and smiled.

He then whispered to Nathial: *"See you soon. I can't wait to introduce you to my wife and daughter."* and with that, he closed his eyes, and passed away.

Paul had suffered a stroke.

After Paul passed, the live-in aide stayed with Nathial and helped him with the preparations for the funeral and services. He spoke at the funeral, then accompanied the funeral procession, as they laid Paul's body to rest.

After the funeral, Nathial gave all the paperwork to the trustees of the estate, to sell the ranch property and donate the money to local widowed residents who had lost their husbands and wives as Paul wanted. He then ensured the live-in aide was generously paid from the proceeds and then packed up what little belongings he had acquired while living with Paul, in a small, easy to carry bag, and headed out the house, with the intent to leave the property, never to return.

Before he left, he created a sign that he nailed on a small piece of wood, and drove it into the soil in the garden.

It read: *"Here worked the kindest man who has ever lived in the modern era. He chose to happily die than to live on, in sadness; for he longed to see his wife and daughter once again. Due to his faithful and noble choice, the next time he opens his eyes, he will."*

Nathial then walked off the ranch, looking back once more, at the small house they once lived in for one last time, smiling fondly, as he walked away.

The Stranger

"This tale of the Stranger is simply not what you may think. Read every line, interpret ahead, don't blink."

One day, a middle-aged man had arrived home and opened his door to find a strange man standing in his living room. The strange man immediately told the man that he would not harm him and that he came just to talk.

The man, feeling very scared and threatened, ran out of the house and called the police.

When the police showed up, they went into the man's house and could find no traces of the intruder. The police told the man to call immediately if he saw the intruder once more. They also posted a car outside the man's house for a few hours, but no one showed up again. The police then left after a few hours of waiting.

The man called a locksmith and changed all the locks in his house that same day. He got an extra lock for the front door and even set up a camera pointed at the door to see if there would be any intruders trying to break in. As he was adjusting the camera, the intruder, whom he saw earlier, was standing behind him.

This startled the man so much that he screamed out and went to grab his phone. The man who was standing there told him not to be scared because he would not harm him, but the scared man, still not listening, reached for his phone.

As the man put his hand in his pocket, he looked up and saw that the stranger was holding his phone in front of him.

The stranger told him that he would give it back to him, but that he should not call the police again, because he didn't know how much time he had left, and all he wanted to do was talk.

"What are you, like the devil or something?"

"*No, certainly not. Please calm down.*"

"How are you in my house? I changed all my locks!"

"*Calm down my Brother. Don't shout. I didn't break in.*"

"What do you want with me?"

"I just want to talk to you."

"About what?" The man asked.

"A few things. But first, calm down. Here's your phone. I don't want to hurt you in any way, shape, or form."

The stranger slowly walked up to the man with his hands up and cautiously handed the man his phone. The stranger then walked away and sat down on the floor in the living room and asked the man to come to sit down. He assured him once again that he would not be harmed in any way, and that the man could trust what he said because he wasn't in the business of lying. The man relieved that the stranger seemed to genuinely want to talk, came and stood by the couch, but refused to sit.

The stranger laughed and said that the man was silly to fear him. He was neither dangerous or harmful to him in any way.

"Why should I believe that?" The man asked.

"Because I'm not. Don't worry. I couldn't harm you if I wanted to. If I did, I would probably be the one harmed."

"Ok? But this is my house. What are you doing here? Can you just leave?"

"*Well, honestly, I could…but I won't. Not before I talk to you.*"

"Ok, alright. Talk, then when you are finished, kindly leave."

"*Well, ok, but it will be much better for us to have a conversation, no?*" Said the stranger.

"I don't know? Is it better?" The man asked.

"*Tell you what, go, bring us something to eat, because we have a lot to talk about, and I know you have some baked mac and cheese in the fridge. Bring me some will you?*"

~Part II~

You're hungry right now?" The man asked, now slightly less threatened.

"*Yeah. We can eat, then we can talk. Again, I promise, I will not hurt you in any way. If you feel better, I can even lay on my belly, let you tie my hands behind my back and everything. Well, maybe leave me one hand, will you? Unless you wanna feed me? I'm ok with that. Anything to make you feel safe.*"

"No, I'm not feeding you. I will get you something, but I'm watching you. If you make one move or try anything, I will call the police and grab a knife. Ok?

"*Ok.*" Said the stranger with a smile.

As the man went to the kitchen, he came up with the idea that he would call the police and tell them quietly that the man had returned.

As he reached for his phone, the guy shouted from the living room that there was really no reason to do that and that he should just bring the food so they could talk after. He said he should hurry, for he was very hungry and wanted to eat.

"How did you know I was gonna get my phone?" The man asked.

"Please my brother, where's the mac and cheese? I told you I'm hungry, and you make good baked mac and cheese. Just bring me some please."

At hearing this, the man, still somewhat apprehensive, brought some mac and cheese for the stranger.

The stranger ate every last drop of the food he had on his plate, said it was good and belched. The stranger had made himself comfortable in the man's house it seemed.

"Ok, so now what do you want to talk about?" The man asked the stranger.

"Well, you tell me." The stranger replied. *"After all, this was all your doing."*

~Part III~

As the stranger stared at the man, he smiled and laughed a little again.

"*So this is where you live huh?*"

"Yes. So?"

"*Well no, it's ok. I'm not judging. You do what you want brother.*"

"I'm not your brother."

"*Well actually…* The Stranger paused mid-sentence. Then he started speaking again.

"*You know what?*"

"What?" The man answered.

"*You surprised me. I never thought you could pull it off. But here you are!*"

"I don't know what you mean, guy."

"*Yeah, you do.*" The stranger replied.

"No, I don't." The man answered again more strongly and annoyed.

"*Hehe, Of course, you don't. Tell you what, I know this is rough for you, so I will just come out and say it. But I don't think you're ready to hear the truth.*"

"What truth?"

"*Eh, I don't know. You were supposed to figure it out yourself.*"

"Figure out what?" The man asked.

"*Well, aren't you the little conman? Aren't you? Trying to get me to talk. You were always a smart guy.*"

"Can you stop playing games and tell me what I was supposed to know? Or what I am supposed to figure out? The man began to get angry. "You come to my house, and hold me here hostage, then you won't tell me what you want?"

"*No one is keeping you hostage, my brother. I just wanted to talk.*"

"Then talk!" The man shouted. He was a man of a short temper. He always had little patience for people who would jerk him around or played games.

As soon as the man shouted, he had a strong headache. It only lasted for five seconds, but during that time, he swore he saw a bright flash of light and what looked like a lot of white linen floating all over the place. He blinked, and it was gone.

"What? What was that? Did you see that?" The man asked.

"*What did you see?* The stranger replied.

"I don't know. It was strange. As soon as I yelled at you, I had a headache, and I saw a lot of white sheets and linen everywhere."

"*White sheets? White Linen?*" The man laughed. "*You saw white linen?*"

"Yeah, it was floating around everywhere. That was so weird."

"*You are too much, brother. The first time you recall something, you see white sheets. That's a good one.*"

"The first time I recall? What does that mean? Can you please tell me?"

"*Ok fine. Since you are taking so darn long, I will tell you. So listen, you did something.*"

"What did I do?"

"*Well, I hate to break it to you, but you aren't human. Well, you weren't previously anyway.*"

"I'm not human?" The man asked. "So then, what am I?"

"*Well, you are a…*"

~Part IV~

It had been now several minutes since the stranger had shown up in the man's home. He had eaten his food. He had made himself comfortable. He had laughed and joked with the man. But now, joking and laughing was for the most part, over with. It was time to get down to business. The news of what the man was, as told to him by the stranger, was met with silence and disbelief. Finally, the man spoke.

"Come on. Really? That's the best you can do? Huh? You expect me to believe you?"

"I'm not lying. I told you, I'm not in the business of lying. Besides, there are others who do it way better than me."

"I'm a man. Not a…"

The stranger interrupted him.

"How do you suppose I got your phone out of your pocket when it was still in your pocket? Hmm? Matter of fact, how did I get into your house when you changed the locks?"

"You're a pickpocket and a thief or a burglar. That's how."

"Now, now. You don't have to call me names. I told you I didn't do anything like that. I walked in."

"But how is that even possible what you said?" The man asked. I just can't be. I have lived all my life as a man.

"Well, you're not, ok? So just accept it."

"Accept it? Are you serious? You come here and tell me something like that, and I'm supposed to accept it?"

"Well, why not? Is that a bad thing?"

"Well, yeah! I mean, how am I…and what happened to cause me to…this is just all so confusing."

"Don't worry. For now, just accept it. We have to discuss some important things."

"Like what?"

"For starters, do you want to stay a man?" The stranger asked.

"What do you mean? Stay a man? Of course, I want to stay a man. What does that even mean?"

"Hey, I'm just doing what you asked."

"What?"

"You asked me to ask you if you wanted to stay a man when we talked next…so I asked you."

"This is insane and crazy. Listen, guy, I need you to leave. I'm done."

The man walked over to the stranger, and now, feeling confident and bold enough to touch the stranger, he reached out his hand to grab his shoulder to force him to get up and leave.

"No, wait, don't touch me so deliberately yet! You're not ready…"

~Part V~

As the man grabbed the stranger, the man experienced a second flash of light. When he opened his eyes, he saw the image of the white linen and sheets again, but this time, the linen seemed to be wrapped around people. As he took a closer look, the linen cleared up to be shaped like people, only bigger. They were all over the room, crowded. As he looked at one of them, the person, now seeing that he was directly looking at him, turned towards him. All the white forms did. They then started walking towards him. The man screamed and closed his eyes.

When he opened them, the stranger was standing in front of him, waving his arms in the air, fiercely, seemingly at the air behind him to move back. The stranger then said: "*Give him some space.*"

"Give who space?" The man asked, confused, and still scared.

"*Don't worry about it. Hey listen, I'm sorry. I should have warned you not to touch me yet. At least, not so deliberately. I knew it would cause you to see what you weren't ready to see.*"

"What was that?" The man asked.

"*You know what that was. You know exactly who they were.*"

"No, I don't. That was scary. Why were all those people in the room suddenly like that?"

"*Ok, so don't be upset.*"

"What is this? What is going on?"

"*I was trying to tell you before; you are not a man.*"

"Oh Jesus, what is happening? What is happening to me!"

The stranger cringed and slinked back a little. Almost as if in sudden pain. The man noticed it and stopped screaming.

"What's wrong with you?"

"*Nothing. It's just…I can't stay here much longer, that's all. Listen, calm down, I promise, you are fine.*"

"No, I'm not fine. One moment I am seeing you, then the next moment, the room is filled with people in white clothes. Is this really true?"

"Yes. But listen, you have to make a choice now."

"What choice?"

"We need to know; do you want to stay a man?" The stranger asked.

"We? Listen, I'm freaking out, guy. Can you please explain to me what is happening?"

The stranger explained again.

"Ok, but if that is true, why would I do that?"

"Well, you said you wanted to see what it was like to live like a man and that you wanted to see how hard it was to live like that. You were simply given permission, and you did it."

"You mean, I "chose" to be a man? To be human?"

"Correct."

"Who chooses that? No one can "choose" who they are. And why? Even if what you say is true, why would I do that?"

"Because you said you had to know for yourself. So, listen, the time is almost up when you have to make a decision. Either stay a man, or…"

"I want to stay a man."

"Really? Despite what you just saw?" Aren't you curious to come back? At this point, if you did want to come back, you still can."

"No, I am a man. I was always a man. I don't want to come back. And come back to where? Where exactly would I be going?"

"Huh. You think you truly know someone."

"What do you mean by that? You don't know me."

The stranger laughed.

"Of course, I do brother. Come on. Do you know how long we've been together? You're funny. Listen, I can't force you to come back, it has to be your decision."

"No, I won't "come" back. Or whatever you want me to do. Just please man, can you please just go?"

~Part VI~

As the men conversed, it was growing later in the afternoon, almost getting dark, and the sun was about to set.

"Tell you what, I will let you see one last time. Don't be scared ok? No one will hurt you."

"Let me see? What? Just please don't make me see what I just…"

The stranger walked behind the man and touched the man on his back. As he did so, the man experienced another flash of light so bright, that he had to squint his eyes closed. When he opened them, an extremely large child-like being, twice his height, in white was leaning over him, two inches from his face, staring directly at him.

To this, the man startled and jumped back, right into the arms of the stranger who was talking to him before, but this time, the stranger had all over white on as well.

"Yes, my brother, you are one of us. See all these people here? You are one of them too. Come back with us. We miss you."

As the man turned around, he saw what looked like hundreds of people, all in white staring at him. He turned around in disbelief and rubbed his eyes as if to make sure he was seeing correctly. As he put his hand to his face, he blinked. When he blinked, he suddenly didn't see the whole white scene anymore. All he saw was the stranger, now dressed back in plain clothes, standing a few feet away.

"Did you finally see my brother?"

"This is crazy. This can't be real."

"I assure you; this is all real. Now, this is your last chance. You have to decide here and now, if you want to come back or no. If you do, you will finally get to see what this is all about. If you choose no, you will stay a man, and I will never come to see you again. Also, you won't remember this ever again."

"The man looked at the stranger. He was smiling at him so warmly. He almost seemed to have his arms outstretched as to beckon him to come closer. The man started walking towards the stranger, almost as if to decide to come with him when he stopped. He remembered that he just wasn't sure if this was all an illusion. Or if this was a trap? Or some weird dream?

He hesitated. Then he stopped walking.

"No, I just can't. This doesn't feel right."

"*So you don't want to come with me. You are choosing to stay a man?*"

"Yes. I don't know how real what I just saw is, but I know I am a man. I don't want to be something else."

"*This your final answer?*"

"Yes."

"*Ok. As you wish.*"

The sun had just set. It was now getting dark. The outside night lights began to turn on.

"*The time has now passed. You will stay as a man.*"

"Ok, now can you just go?"

"*I'm already gone. Take care, my brother. In my opinion, you have chosen quite p…*"

As the man turned around, he wondered why he was standing alone in his living room. He went to the kitchen to find the fridge door open. He wondered if he had gone to the fridge to get something and forgot to get it.

~Part VII~

*W*hat was his decision?" One of them asked.

"*He chose to stay and wallow with the fallen beings.*"

"*He chose this?*"

"*Yes.*"

"*He can suffer and die with them then.*"

"*Yes, but unlike us, he now gets a chance.*"

"*Wait…a chance…Oh yes. Of course.*"

"*Yes. It seems he made the right choice.*"

"*Had he come back; he would be doomed like the rest of us. But since he stayed a human, he has a chance, a chance for forgiveness.*"

After they were all thrown out, of the countless zillions of them, one of them came back, imploring that he made a terrible mistake and that he knows he should not have taken the other side. He left the rest of them alone and did not join in any plans to cause Man to fail. After Adam's fall, he implored that he had had nothing to do with it, and begged for mercy, asking to live and be as the humans were for all time until the final punishment should come.

He sought to be allowed to become a human and stay a human. He said he would live his life the same way and suffer along with them, for he preferred to live this way and share the small light of joy the humans felt when living on the earth and embracing God. This he felt was so precious, as the alternative would be to keep the company of him, who caused all this, and this he refused to do. Also, he would be adamant and careful to never join the wrong side ever again.

He was granted his request.

God would not permit him to suffer in perpetual torment, as some now believe God does or will do to any created being. He would instead, live lives of human joy and suffering over and over once each for six times, then once more, for the seventh time. After this, he would then die and cease to exist, all without knowing the truth of his origins, as his memory was removed from him. God would then decide the fate of his now mortal soul, based on how he lived as a human, and not for the decision he made to rebel the first time.

His *"Brothers"* were some who wanted him to come back, but he ultimately made the right choice to stay, as God had placed him. He reasoned that this was better than the fate now awaiting them, as he dreaded the final punishment, and did not want to die this way. He still very much, loved God and wanted to show it through this act of repentance.

God, in mercy, spared him the final punishment and allowed him to live his remaining time this way. Six times, a fallen angel came to him to get him to turn back into an angel, and six times he refused, unknowing of what fate he would have in store for him should he agree. However, he successfully denied them each of the six times, choosing to stay a man. The fallen angels became jealous and struggled to do everything to make this once angel come back to their side, but they were always unsuccessful. Did God forgive him? Would he get the privilege of the sacrifice? The privilege of redemption? This was not fair they deemed. Nonetheless, these questions would not be answered for them, for they were no longer allowed to disturb or bother him again. After this, there would be no more indeed, for this was his seventh time.

Part IV

A Few Poems by My Precious Mother

"Favour is deceitful, and beauty is vain: but a woman that feareth the Lord, she shall be praised."

Proverbs 31:30 KJV

God Brought Me To His School (His Spirit Within)

I once stood at crossroads and wondered which way to go,

GOD said *"go forward; I have chosen a garden where you can grow."*

"This garden has some weeds, but there is a spot I have in reserve,

Many trees have grown in the fertile land that I have preserved."

The Lord brought me to school, his personal university,

"Here will be your chance and your opportunity.

Trust me, for I am always close, close in proximity,

I am just a prayer away; I am never out of your vicinity."

A dark voice asked me where I thought I was going,

The wind rose against me and began a furious blowing.

You are too old," it said, "you cannot make it in,"

But God said, *"Go Forward. My Spirit is Within."*

God said, *"Continue to look up, look to the hills up yonder"*

I was brought to his school and accepted without much ponder.

Yet the other voice told me that I cannot learn at this stage,

But God said, *"I am your Master Teacher at any age."*

The other voice said, you can't deal with the stress,

But God said, *"Don't worry my child, I will give you success."*

He sent a message again, because I was filled with doubts in my ability,

He let me know he would give me the blessing in its entirety.

Each class got heavier and heavier, it almost drove me to the brink,

Because to make it, it is sometimes harder than you think.

I thought of the others before me who had made it through,

I prayed to God to ask him for help to make it, too.

The journey is not friendly, many prayers were sent for the day,

God said, *"My Grace is sufficient, just continue on your way."*

Sometimes I saw things as if it was blocking my view,

God said, *"Don't worry my child. I am right here beside you."*

He told me to look up. Look up to the hills and see,

Have faith and behold, yes, *"Behold The Almighty Me."*

"You have not chosen me, But I have chosen you",

"And whatsoever you ask in my name in faith, I shall do."

With God's grace, I am now bound for my graduation,

I look forward with gratitude to God and a celebration.

I look back now, and it is so very clear,

I see one set of prints, and I know it was Him who carried me there.

He covered me with his loving and tender care,

There was nothing for me to worry about, nothing for me to fear.

Lord thank you for my family who supported me on the way,

Thank you for answering all our prayers day by day.

Thank you for the wisdom that you have shared,

Your blessings and mercy show that you deeply cared.

Now I tell this story to you once more, through thick and thin,

All things are possible when *His Spirit is Within*.

Gratitude

Lord, I want to show my gratitude to you since my new life has begun,

Is there anything I could see, if you were to show my life, rerun?

How many times did I not say thanks, in just a word or two,

Or say "Lord I love thee" Just to name a few.

Lord please remind me to say "please" and "thank you".

For they are simple words I forget to tell you.

Often life is taken for granted, and time slips by somehow,

Lord I am saying "Thank You" for what you have done for me right now.

So many things we promise to do, but they don't get done,

Lord please grant me grace to live a life of gratitude for now and the long run.

You promised you will return for the obedient one's who love you,

Help me Lord to be thankful, while waiting patiently and true.

O Lord, I love you, I love you.

Jesus Is Our Hope, An Explanation

As we await Jesus' coming, with great anticipation,

We must now ask for grace to let go of all sinful gratification.

For the Lord, he is God, and he has paid for our Salvation

This poem is a message, a brief explanation.

When we are tempted to do things with a bad intention,

Let us look at the word of God, we must pay strict attention.

Jesus came to the earth to give us a sweet redemption.

So that the second death for us will be an exemption.

Let us by his grace, turn away from sin and degradation

For Jesus in his mercy gave us full justification

He also granted us his precious sanctification

And with his blood, he gave us a purification.

Let us keep away from all forms of fornication

And look to the Lord for Emancipation

The Lord, He is God, and he looks down on his congregation

Let us ask for grace in our life's travels to meet our destination,

And to help us with our sinful inclination.

So that he can keep us from utter destruction and devastation.

Come now let us pray for God's Rejuvenation.

For those who do not love and accept Him; this is a serious consternation,

Without him as their personal savior, working to salvation.

For when Jesus comes, he will have books filled with full names and no abbreviations.

Each person's name will have the proper pronunciation.

Then the Angels will be dispatched for the great mobilization,

Those who have died will be raised with their Godly certification.

And those who are alive will be caught up in this great transportation.

So let us end this with this wonderful annotation,

For when Jesus comes again, there will be a great celebration.

And indeed, a wonderful Coronation.

Lord, I Want To Smile

Lord, I want to smile, as I walk along the way,

I want to smile because someone might be having a bad day.

It can be like medicine, and it can tell of joy,

For a cause this good, virtue I must employ.

Lord, if my smile can be the remedy for someone's pain,

Please give me a beautiful smile, it won't be given in vain.

Lord, I want to smile just to say thank you for my day,

I want to smile to chase the blues away.

Teach me to smile when I rise in the morning,

And in the evening, at the new day's dawning.

When I smile, I know someone, somewhere will smile back,

So Lord, I will smile with someone I come into contact.

A smile can be priceless to someone who needs a friend,

Yes, a smile is worth having, even when hard times are around the bend.

Lord, please grant me a smile today, for it cannot be bought,

This is my longing plea, only for this I truly sought.

A smile can provide a ray of sunshine and laughter over sadness,

This is why I want to smile dear Lord, for I want to bring, only gladness.

Good News

If I could spread the news from up above,

I'll tell everyone I meet, that God is love.

First, I'll ask those around, their point of view,

And let them know there's one, whose love is true.

I'll tell them the good news about our beloved Christ

Reaffirming that yes! He paid the ultimate price.

I'll ask God to give me the courage to go to every home and hut

And listen to everyone's stories, no if's, and's, or but's.

Then we can agree, this realization makes the cut,

Sin, with its unhappy state, has us all in a rut.

But I'll tell them to take heart, that there's good news,

I pray that they would listen to my point of view's.

Our Savior Jesus Christ, The Lord bore all our sin,

He carried the whole lot; we can have peace from within!

I'll ask God to help me remind those who have forgotten,

that Jesus lived among mankind, yes, Christ the only-begotten.

I'll tell them, he died for you and he died for me,

And tell them again, we have the chance to live sin-free.

His love was destined to us from the start,

So this is what we should let abide in our heart,

And ask him for grace to let our hate depart.

Then we can move to action, we can all play a part.

Then we will be one, and all in unity,

And soon it will spread, throughout the community,

Yes, it will travel to every city and every dome

To every capital city, every country we roam.

Love can change the world, it's the one principal thing

Just think of how much our hearts will sing

Yes, I'll ask God to help me in my neighborly walk,

To give me a voice and I'll talk and I'll talk.

Jesus loves us all, our joy has begun,

For on the cross, the victory was won.

I'll ask God to send all help from above

for if I could, I'll start with Jesus and his love

I'll tell them the good news, to one and to all

He will give us his spirit, his power he'll install,

And then the latter rain will soon come to fall,

and all voices will be lifted up to give the last call.

Let's all be ready, Jesus is coming again,

Oh, love, his love! what sweet refrain.

A gift to us, the only thing that can change the world
again.

Let love fall upon our hearts, let love in its fullness reign.

Yes, if I could change the world through love for you,

I'll tell you what I'll say, I'll tell you what I'll do.

I'll tell them and tell them again; God's love is true.

This is my good news today, my good news to you.

Part V

A Few Benedictions

"Now unto him that is able to keep you from falling, and to present you faultless before the presence of his glory with exceeding joy; To the only wise God our Saviour, be glory and majesty, dominion and power, both now and ever. Amen.

Jude 1:25-25 KJV

Benedictions

When We Sing

Our bodies respond to hearing the song of Praise,

Our very souls cry out when our voices we Raise.

We stare upwards at you, and longingly Gaze,

At the angels who bask in the light of your glorious Rays.
Amen.

Two Blessings

Two blessings to you, as you leave this Place,

One of hope and one of loving Grace,

May God look upon you, and shine his Face,

And your heart with him, forever Interlace. Amen.

A True Friend

Jesus, our one true loving Friend,

Our hearts with you we want to Mend,

May these words to you in love, Ascend,

For you promised to be with us to the very End. Amen.

Your Love Sustains Us

We walk sustained, yet undeserving Of,

The mercy sent from up Above,

The spirit of the purest, whitest Dove,

For you are the only habitation of unceasing Love. Amen.

A Cry for Mercy

Dear Jesus, we know that we would Be,

Completely lost and broken without Thee,

Please break the true bread of life to Me,

Grant us your omnipotent love and Mercy. Amen.

Raise Us

Your grace, Dear Lord, we long to Receive,

Come back to gather your children and Retrieve,

Our faith rests in you, we truly Believe,

Please bring us to wondrous places we never Conceived. Amen.

Epilogue: God Be With You Till We Meet Again

I truly hope you enjoyed this book. My only wish is for it to serve as a little bit of encouragement and spiritual inspiration and motivation, as you read through these pages.

If I was able to bless you, even for a moment with these words, then I succeeding in shining a little light on you, and as such, God is pleased, for he wants his children to always have hope and confidence for a bright and hopeful future.

Please also spread the word. I want as much people to read these words as possible. The goal is to get more people to read these hopeful and comforting words, and leave a small imprint on their minds in faith.

Please feel free to contact me anytime at my email at kingsley.nurse1@gmail.com.

May you stay well until we can hopefully meet again!

God's *Blessings* on you, now and forever.

-Kingsley

Made in the USA
Middletown, DE
07 December 2020